GOD IN MY UNBELIEF

GOD IN
MY UNBELIEF

By

J. W. STEVENSON

HARPER & ROW, PUBLISHERS

NEW YORK AND EVANSTON

*No living person is recognisably portrayed
in this book; and all names are fictitious*

First published in the United States of America 1963

LIBRARY OF CONGRESS CATALOG CARD NUMBER: 63-14960

Lord, I believe; help thou my unbelief.

ST. MARK 9, 24

I

I SAW them first through the tinted glass of the vestry window; in the blue I could see only the blurred outline of their faces, in the red every feature—an anticipation of how some were to be known to me almost with the certainty of heaven's face-to-face, and others were to be mistakenly judged.

They moved into the old church on the Knowe to take their vows; perhaps not reckoning, many of them, on all that it meant to be bound to a minister, as I certainly did not reckon on what would happen to me because I was bound to them.

I had made my vow in another country church three months after my father's death. In that moment the years of uncertainty had seemed to be put behind me as I knelt at the Communion table beside which his body had been laid. But I had found, like others, that it is one thing to wish to serve the highest and another to be willing to be made fit for the serving.

Even on this day, within Crainie Kirk, with its one ancient wall and the remainder of its structure adapted to create an extra "laird's loft" a hundred years before, different voices were speaking in the name of the Church at the moment when most of all I wanted to hear one voice clearly.

The words of Scripture were in my ears, giving me my warrant—that I was to stand before these people in Christ's stead, beseeching them to be reconciled to God. The ancient prayer was said for me, that I might present myself a living

7

sacrifice. Assurance was sought from me that zeal for the glory of God, love to the Lord Jesus Christ and a desire for the salvation of men were my " great motive and chief inducement " in entering the office of the holy ministry.

But another voice was counselling me in other tones. I must not expect miracles; I must hasten slowly; I must keep the peace . . . The minister of a neighbouring parish was giving me my " charge " from the plush-backed pulpit set against the austere Norman walls. He was speaking out of long experience of the ways of men in these upland glens, and I know he loved the Kirk. But he seemed to leave me thinking that the great factor in my ministry would be my capacity to handle difficult situations tactfully and to keep on good terms with all my people.

In the evening all the parish was gathered in the village hall, the lairds and their families in the front seats, the farm-workers packed at the rear, and the rest, mixed together in between, with a good number of Crainie men from beyond the parish back to " see the new man in." There had not been a new man for nearly fifty years; this was a day in parish history, though the parish was no longer regarded as it used to be by the authorities in high places; the old love of familiar place and people, and the loyalty springing from it, were not dead. The village shop had its half-holiday a day earlier than usual, as it did at a Coronation; the children went home early from school to take their share in the preparation; even the beasts knew there was something afoot, for the cattlemen were round the fields two hours earlier and shepherds were minding their neighbours' hirsels. However mingled it might be with other motives, there was some sort of expectation, though it could not perhaps have been put into words by any of them.

I had been brought to preach a few weeks before, so that I

might prove myself acceptable to them; but I knew in my heart that I was there also to be the minister of what could not be easily acceptable.

On this night of welcome my friends were with me to vouch for me. They made the most of any reputation I had in my studies; they commended me, with the feast of story that was expected of them, as one who would make himself at home amongst the people of Crainie. But they did not say that all this could be " as sounding brass and tinkling cymbal " without the love for which they could not vouch.

I looked out across the faces of the people and loved them for the expectation that was in them, and for the kindness I was to come to know so well. But I did not understand then the mystery of the Church in which we had been sharing that day as God's people—that He sets us in the community of His love while we are yet, by all the signs, unfit for it; that He binds us one to another before we seem ready to be bound.

In the years that followed I was often to be perplexed by this. I was to be cast down by what seemed to deny all that the Church was intended to be. But I was to learn also why these things are so; why, under one aspect, the Church seems to be made up of men and women no better than the rest, and, under another, has the look of heaven.

What happened in Crainie in these next years was a small thing, weighed against what men were reading in their newspapers; but to learn how God saves ten men is to learn also how He can save a city.

2

THE VILLAGE of Crainie has an appearance of casualness, though it was built house by house where blacksmith and miller and weaver needed to be for their work. It is far enough into the hills to be its own world—not far enough from the cities to escape their influence.

It has often been on the defensive against the outsider. It built its hill-top forts in the days when the Angles from North Europe came against the Kingdom of Strathclyde, and men and beasts had to be hurriedly herded from the valleys to places of safety; and it has believed itself to be under attack of a different kind from other intruders. Witches were burned at the Knowe long after the present church was built, because they were opening a door which ought to have been kept closed; and another hill has the marks of what was done with the Beltane fire to ward off the dark powers.

The marks of Crainie's fears are still there on the land; and it was not long before I saw them in the lives of the people. They had learned through long generations how to protect themselves against the more disturbing mysteries, and to make their own world out of the things of which they were certain. But they kept their fears alive in the very shutting of the door.

Colonel Baillie said that the old coal-stove which used to be in the church had always been the symbol of Crainie for him: an uncertain fire, slow to burn and sometimes nothing but smoke—but warm enough when you had the right way of the wind.

They were cautious about anything new, especially a new minister. " They'll no' rush at ye," Kennedy the beadle warned me; " gie them time, gie them time . . . Crainie aye tak's a twalmonth to look at a man."

Jen Pringle, the wise woman of the village, who had seen generations come and go in Crainie for seventy-five years, had her advice. She hoped I would fit into the ways of Crainie folk. I would have to learn for myself who were to be trusted and who were to be watched, how to deal with the difficult ones, how not to heed certain ones at all—above all, to "gang warily " and not to expect too much. "We've aye been a queer folk in Crainie—and we dinna change."

They had their standards of honesty and fair-dealing, too, which did not change; they were a steady people.

I did not worry just then about their cautiousness. I became absorbed in the life of the community and began to learn its skills. I worked in the manse garden, its plots and its paths as they had been for two hundred years, and took advice from the gardeners of the big houses. I learned how to put hay in a coil; when the roads were blocked with snow I was taught by the roadmen how to cast; I sat at the roadside with the dyker and found how his stones were set so that they would lock together without mortar. I walked the red roads and over the hills—when the storms were sweeping the glen and the shepherds were bringing the ewes in-by, and in the moonlight when the woods were quiet. The twenty miles of field and hill, woods and running water, became my life.

I remembered how I had sat, as a boy, watching the glint of the sun across the bare fields on a dull March day, feeling it like an immediate movement from the Creator's hands. It came back to me now. Night and day were something given afresh; the storm and the quiet were something prepared for us as part of the raw material for our living, no less immediate because it could all be tracked and plotted across the oceans, the bread no less a gift because it was given us through many human hands.

There must always have been this in men's minds before we contrived a world of our own to shut out the immensities: a strangeness in the earth, as if every movement had its distant source in creation present in it—as if creation itself were a perpetual living gift.

We gathered together every Sunday in the church with this strangeness around us, below the hills which have nurtured the beasts as long as human memory goes back—and every flower on the hillside springing up in faithfulness exactly as our fore-fathers knew them; the primeval rock and the stonecrop creeping round it, death and life intertwined.

We were surrounded by a mystery we could not fathom. When we stood listening to the unchanging cries of the birds we seemed to be just where our fathers were and to know no more than they did, in spite of all our discoveries. We were part of the mystery; it was within us; we could not get outside it; it kept us strangers in the earth. We did not know whence we came or whither we went. And then within the church walls another voice fell upon us. We were made akin to an abiding certainty beyond the mystery. We were called sons of God. We were claimed brethren of Christ. But this voice, too, had its mystery; and in our day we were so much given to measuring and plotting the forces of life and using nature for our gain that we were inclined to close our minds both to the mystery of our world and to the mystery that lies beyond it. We made little allowance for anything which did not come within our immediate experience, and in that were less wise than our forefathers who peopled their world with fairies and figures of doom.

There was little awe in Crainie that we were " moving about in worlds half-realised," gaining or losing the heavenly Kingdom, bearing in our bodies the marks of the Lord Jesus, or denying Him.

Donald Mathieson, for example, had no use for the Kirk; he had " cast out " with the minister twenty years before; and he had never been aware of being any the worse for it. He no longer heard the sermons—but he had never remembered them anyhow by the time he had had his dinner. There was no fear in this big straight-backed man, as Crainie saw him, taking his long, slow stride amongst them. But there were some things he did not want to face; and one of them was what the Bible had said to him, and something in his heart had confirmed, twenty years before, about forgiving seventy times seven. Rather than face that he had kept the argument he had had with the minister warm in his mind; he had known that he was right; and so he was; and every time he went over it with his friends he became more convinced of it. It set his mind at rest about his break with the Kirk; and he never stopped to ask himself why it needed to be set at rest, and from what it needed to be set at rest. He did not know that he was using what had happened with the minister to ward off what his Maker was commanding. His arguments had been a cloak for twenty years to hide it from himself.

He would never again, he said, walk up the church road on a Sunday morning; but that road was not the road to the minister's sermon only; it was a road which had other decisions; and he was afraid to take it. He had measured out his life, what was to be expected of him, and what his duty demanded. Thus far he would go and no farther. He had no ear for anything beyond.

Yet this was the man whose solid step sounded on the wooden footbridge every evening at a quarter to nine, when he went to the single-end where his mother lived alone, to carry her coal and wind her clock and see that she was set for the night.

He had no thought beyond his duty. But there had been a man once with His last thought on the cross for His mother, that she should have a home and that His disciple should be a new kind of son to her and be a watcher of her old age.

The concern of this man on the cross and this man in Crainie belonged together. They were from the same source. From there too had come the urge to forgive which he had choked and stifled for twenty years. He had allowed himself to be bidden to what he had decided he could do; he had refused to be bidden where he was determined not to go—within the steady stride of his life obedience and disobedience to the mystery of God's love; compassion which he allowed to move him; forgiveness against which he put up the barrier because he was afraid where it would lead him; and he did not understand either.

3

THERE WERE two sides to others besides Donald Mathieson, as I saw when I first called at Wellwood and went on to a ploughman's cottage on the home farm. The doctor had asked my help in bringing a seven-year-old girl to hospital.

" Take a look at the walls," he said on the telephone, " and you will see why this has happened."

The child's mother was at the door, carrying an empty pail. When I offered to get the water for her she shook her head; I would not know how to get it. I followed her to the middle of a field to a pool of water, surrounded on three sides by a fence, used by man and beast alike. Two waterfowl rose with a flurry of wings. The water had to be taken in jugfuls and allowed to settle between each.

" We're always promised water in the house . . . But we've been here five years."

In the hospital I asked the doctor if the girl was going to die just because of the condition of that house. He could not deny it. There were no regulations devised then which could compel the owner of the farm to see to the repairs; and no help available to him if he could not afford it—which John Sanderson of Wellwood certainly could.

All the way home I remembered another child, lying flushed and restless in bed, and Sanderson pacing up and down his library repeating " Everything possible must be done for her."

Within the same man this tenderness and this hardness, this agony of concern and this indifference. His own girl must have everything she needed—but the farm must be made to yield the maximum profit; wages and upkeep must be kept to the minimum—even when the upkeep meant what another little girl required for her health.

It was not only social caste which divided Wellwood from its farm cottages; it was something within John Sanderson himself, a cleavage between his pity and his profits. He was still wanting to do opposite things with his life. The same impulse from God was obeyed or driven out of reckoning.

And John Sanderson was not alone in it. This was not just inconsistency within human nature. It was something which split human nature in two; and it had its origins far back in human life. Something had been set in the heart of man which made him capable of thinking more of the good of others than of his own, and of laying down his life for people he did not know; and something else within him kept telling him not to be a fool, to get out of life what he could for himself. Whatever we believed about ourselves, this could not be denied: we were selfish; and we were willing to sacrifice. What forces had strengthened the one and the other, what fears had prevented us from making our decision between them, was the mystery. We could say it was a mystery and leave it at that. But it did not leave us. It divided our mind. It took away our peace. It bewildered and confused us. We were living in the accumulated confusion of the generations before us, though we had their light, too, to walk by.

So we had to contrive a life together in which evil impulses would be restrained for the good of the community; but that did not take the evil impulses away; they continued to work their havoc within; they found their own new outlets. Beneath the surface life of civilised habit the old lawlessness was still there; and there was the stronger temptation to shut our eyes to it because a way had been found which seemed to keep it in check.

Some day, as the doctor had said, there would be regulations to ensure that the farm cottages at Wellwood had not rotten walls; the ploughmen and their families would be safeguarded against a man who kept his own house weather-tight and let his worker's kitchen drip damp. But the heart of a man like John Sanderson would not be changed by new regulations. There would no longer be open evidence of what was within his heart. Perhaps he would seem then to be a better man than he was, when some of the signs of his hardness had been taken away. Perhaps with all these new measures to restrain us when we were disregarding our neighbour's good we might be more deeply deceived than ever about what was in us. It was right that we should be restrained; it was necessary that the State should stand by those who were at the mercy of other men's selfishness; but the more restraint we had the more we might be content to be law-abiding and the less we might think of the anger and contempt which broke no laws but continued to break human hearts and to sin against God.

The Crainie the stranger sees on the roads is the law-abiding Crainie which has set itself in order for the accomplishing of its work, the Crainie of folk who depend on one another and on the whole can get on with one another, except where the raw edges of one man's life rub on his neighbour's.

But anyone living for a while amongst us knew that there was another Crainie behind the doors: a Crainie where men have something in their lives with which they do not know how to deal; one moment reaching out in impulsive kindness, and the next holding back from the forgiving word. Behind the doors are men and women not knowing often what to make of themselves, ordering their life by what can be expected of them, telling you what they consider is the least they can do for a neighbour in need, and what is more than they can stand from him.

Yet they went on doing the kindness which never could be proved worth-while. They kept searching to find how they might get faith; and it was in them. They did not rule the whole of their lives by carefulness. They would set aside everything to be able to give help to a neighbour, even when it could not be certain that the help would be worth-while. A man would walk two miles up the glen to try to teach a spastic child to read, without estimating whether he was making anything of it. When an old woman got regularly to the end of her resources because of what she spent on liquor she would be set on her feet again by some impulse which they could not argue about—over and over again, seventy times seven, when they might well have said that they were finished with her, that she was not worth helping. They did not say it, because of some faith in them, something which made them hold to their compassion when by any reasoning they should have abandoned it. It was planted in them, though at other times they might exert all their will-power to do only what decency dictated, and might speak as if that was all there was to it.

And it was these people, set in a law-abiding community which had so much in it, good and bad, that did not conform to law, drawing their sustenance from it, having their character moulded by it, who were also the Church of Christ in Crainie —the same people. The Church roll and the public roll bore the same names, except for a handful who had forfeited Church membership by long neglect. These men and women who lived day by day together, employers and employed, opposed in politics, differing in their regard for one another, given to sacrificing and to words of hurt, were also a divine community, the people of God in Crainie.

That was the strangest thing in Crainie. They could have belonged, without strangeness, to some association for the advancement of Christian ideals. If the church had been only a place where the minister exhorted and advised, where we were recalled to higher things after the mundane work of the week, there would have been no strangeness. But we were brought together and spoken to out of God's Word as if we were already in the company of the saints, called to do the work of Christ while we had scarcely allowed Him to begin His work on us.

Had we any right to be there? What was this Church of Christ in Crainie? Was it so broad that it could include the whole community of Crainie, just because its people had taken some sort of vows, with varying degrees of understanding and sincerity? And if so broad, why spoken to as if it were a body of people committed and embarked upon living the life of the Kingdom of God in a world not yet ready for it? The community of Crainie, as its neighbours knew it, was nothing out of the ordinary—but, if it were to obey what was said to it when it met as the community of Christ on Sunday, it would have stood out, a marked place, like a city set on a hill.

A community like Crainie posed many questions. Its minister could fail by giving them an idea of the Church so wide that a man would consider it a natural part of being in the community that he should belong to the local church. He could fail by setting before them a Church to which only men and women of great faith rightly belonged, and others belonged with less right and on lower terms. And he could fail by not reckoning on the contradictions which were in the community's daily life.

Not many of the Crainie folk seemed to have any clear idea what their Church was, beyond the assembling of themselves together on Sunday for the preaching of the Word and for prayer and praise. They were a community during the week in virtue of work done together and life shared with their neighbours—but they did not appear to think of themselves at all as a special kind of community as they sat around the Lord's Table, a people called to a life different from the ordinary life of men.

I was unsure myself in my speaking to them. I belonged to their community; I lived with them as one of themselves; I shared the common lot; I spoke as they did about the things that pleased us and the things that annoyed us. And then I went to the little kirk on the Sunday and, taking the words of the Lord upon my lips, I called them God's people; I set before them the commands to a life which ordinary human nature cannot compass; I upbraided them for falling short in their obedience. But I did not make clear what their obedience was, why the people of the Church should be a different kind of community, the same men and women as people of God and as people of the community's daily work, obedient to their heavenly calling yet involved every day with the same kind of fellow-workers and in the same kind of work. I did not interpret for them these strange impulses which led them, now to think more of the good of others than of their own, now to be so obsessed by what they wanted for themselves that they had no thought for anybody else; now to see the good of Crainie only in fairness of dealing, leaving every man in peace to do what he liked, now as a community willing to bind itself together and sacrifice for a great cause.

I was shown often how little it seemed to mean to them to belong to the Church of Christ. And I was confused in my own mind between the community of the prevailing life and customs of men and the community—the same people— gathered in the house of God, to whom almost unbelievable promises were made and from whom the apparently impossible was expected.

Could it be that God set His seal upon us, because of so tenuous an act of faith as ours sometimes was? By the parents' wish that their children should be baptised, because everybody else had their children baptised? By vows taken with little preparation or understanding? How much, how little, was required of us to become a " people of God," under promise of His grace?

Or was it that He called us of His own grace, and that we only took the first stumbling steps towards Him? But even that laid on us the responsibility for taking the step, to do what made it possible for Him to bestow the grace. We seemed to be left with the power to enable Him, or disable Him; and that was not the Gospel of victorious love.

We must at least begin with this: that the Church was for all in Crainie, for Christ had died for all. Christ had borne in His own body on the tree the sins of all men. We were all caught up and embodied in Him there, believers and un-believers, good and bad. The Church, which is His body, must somehow have all men caught up and embodied within it, in Crainie as everywhere, whether they yet believe or not, however bad or good they may be. The Church is theirs, though it is nothing to them and they still pass by. The Church in Crainie is for all Crainie.

And we must see those who seek truly, and take their vows, as the first-fruits, the forerunners of all who will come after. They are not necessarily better men; they are men who have seen a light, however faint it seems, and have come towards it. But, while they are still wondering about the light, whether the world's darkness will overcome it, they hear a voice saying " Ye are the light of the world."

This is the miracle of the Church. But did it, in fact, happen in Crainie?

Perhaps it is because we often cannot hold this mystery in our minds that we are driven to speak of the Church with conflicting and contradictory voices, as my counsellors had done at my ordination. We make the Church seem easy for all—and do not let men hear themselves being called to be saints. Or we set before them the high and holy way—and turn them from it because it is too high and they know they cannot attain to it.

The contradictions are fundamental to our condition at every level—we are people at one moment ready to give up everything for someone in need and the next prepared to get what we want for ourselves whatever it means to anybody else, and we create a community which orders its life so that the evil in men may be restrained and then is dissatisfied because it is left without the incentives which call out the best in men.

Whatever these contradictions portend, at least they compel us to ask which kind of people we are meant to be, what has gone wrong in us that we are in such contradiction and how it is to be overcome. There is a mystery both in our goodness and in our evil.

And it is these very contradictions which are the clue to the miracle. The Church is God taking men in these dilemmas and delivering them into new life. We are not to stay outside because we are like that; we are to come within because we are like that.

As I began to understand this it was no longer an offence that the Church of Christ in Crainie held so many who did not yet look like the people of God. They were not wrong to be within. But when they came did they believe the ineffable words spoken to them which claimed them for all that they were not yet but must become? Now were they the sons of God—now, though it did not yet appear what they would be.

4

It was not easy in Crainie to think of ourselves breaking away from other people and being the first to do something new. Together we made up the community, where we did not wish to be thought different from others; and together we made up the Church where we were called to be different—but we were the community first. We saw one another as neighbours and fellow-workers, people with fixed characters, before we saw one another as men and women in whom Christ was making all things new. We were predisposed to think of our neighbour remaining as he was and of ourselves remaining as our neighbour had known us. Yet, if this Church of Christ were true, there must always be some to be the first to break out of this circle of acceptance and resignation to things as they are—the first in a family to " dare to stand alone."

The community, in which we came to know one another, formed the pattern of our life; and behind the community was the nation, organised for its industry and its commerce, imposing its shape upon us: what was considered to be most worth seeking, what made up a " good time " for human beings. Because we lived in a small community it was harder to throw off the influences of the world—by the time the world's pressures had reached us they were respectable, indistinguishable from a decent life. We absorbed them; we took them for granted. They moulded our community unseen, and never in such a way as to shock us. We were sure we still remained the same men and women, with our standards of what was fair and just and right for men to do.

We went to church on Sunday, almost the whole community on Sacrament Day, and a good proportion on other days, to be reminded how far we still fell short of what we ought to be. We were the community at prayer. But what were we praying for—for our community? We were giving God the glory—but what was He doing in Crainie for which we wished to glorify Him? We were not expecting the community of Crainie to be any way different from one year's end to the other. We were expecting, perhaps, that we might be better in ourselves, more patient, more brotherly, better-tempered; but how was the community to be better as a community? In what way could it be different? We were not the community of Crainie offering itself before God to be re-shaped, re-made, as the people of God, whatever other men did.

Where could that begin? Where could we break out of this acceptance of the world? Somebody had to begin repenting of being the kind of community we were, being disturbed about it. Some few, perhaps; it had always been by the few that the city had been saved. But was I to begin looking for the few, hand-picking them? Or did I leave them to reveal themselves? And what part had my preaching to play in raising up the witness of the few?

I began to think differently about my preaching. I was there to comfort, to speak peaceably to God's people, to confirm them in their faith, to preach Christ Jesus and His atoning sacrifice. But the Word was also to be sharp as a two-edged sword, to the cleaving asunder of the false in men's lives; it was to pierce this resignation to things as they are, this accept-

ance of what other men impose on us. How else were the
people of God to repent and be a light to the world around
them?

My preaching must not flinch from being that word. It
could not evade judgment on the nation, what it was setting
before us in our common life, what it was telling us to seek
after, what it was warning us not to do. This, too, moulded
our life in Crainie. We could not repent without having new
judgment of the national community which set these standards
for us.

I was wrestling in mind, like many others at the time, about
the issues of peace as the threat of world war came closer.
Had the Church nothing more to do than hope and pray for
peace, to hold up an ideal before men which they had in their
minds already—to proclaim the certainty that some day the
swords would be beaten into ploughshares? Was there nothing
to be done now as followers of Him who broke the power of
sin by the way of the Cross? Were we called to nothing more
than to hope, and in the meantime to take the way which
everybody took? Were we to be just as other men here,
though called to be different from other men elsewhere? Did
it really mean that we could live by our Christian standards in
things less important, less critical, but here we must live by the
world's wisdom, here we must conform—Christ's way only
for the less serious evils?

When I preached like this I roused anger. I was being
disloyal to my country; I was bringing politics into the pulpit;
I was preaching appeasement.

Colonel Baillie remonstrated with me. " You'll lose your
influence," he said. " Can't you see you have won their
friendship—and now you're throwing it away?" It was like
the voice from my ordination service again. We seemed to be

making the commandment of God of no effect; we were regarding as inevitable the very conditions from which the world was to be saved; we were accepting evil as the permanent state of the world, as a necessity to which we must bow. The life to which Christ called us was to be rejected as impracticable for the great evils of mankind.

Yet, when I look back on it, I know that I was often projecting my own dilemma into the political scene; the issues went deeper than I understood. I was myself confused about how to keep evil in check, even in Crainie; how much weight to give to the powers of coercion and restraint, and how much to the redeeming powers of the spirit. I could rebut the charge that I was preaching appeasement; yet within the community of Crainie I had perhaps been concerned overmuch just to keep the peace.

There were some lesser traditions in our community, too, which seemed to transgress the commandment of God. I encountered one of them when we were making our parish preparations for an occasion of national rejoicing. I spoke against it in the Parish Committee because it had proved in the past to be a source of temptation to boys of school age.

I did not find much support. People would expect what other communities were having, and they themselves had always had. This was a community occasion, not a Kirk one.

They did not say, but they obviously meant: " We are not to think of ourselves just now as the people of God—let that be kept for another time." It was another sign of the division we had made between the practical life of the community and the aspiration towards better things which was supposed to be religion. There was a feeling amongst some that the minister had lost his position by attempting to make this change, and failing.

Perhaps, then, it was in individuals that the break with this resignation to the world's ways had to be made—and who more likely than a man come to disaster and compelled to begin life again?

But I did not find it any easier with an alcoholic than I had with the Parish Committee. He did not require to be convinced of his weakness and the shame it brought to his family and to his profession of the Christian faith.

" I'll keep myself out of the way until I've taken a grip of myself," was all he said. That was how he could mitigate the scandal and show respect for the Church and what it stood for.

I had tried to say that the grace of God would be sufficient for his need if he would make the break with the past. But I was still leaving him to make the break; he whose will-power had gone was to summon up enough will-power to master his weakness. He was being left alone to the effort, except for the assurance that I stood by him. We said we were leaving it to God; but it was without being ready to be fellow-workers with Him. We had no way—we who were committed to bear one another's burdens—of bearing this man's burden, helping him in the first steps of his decision, giving him conviviality of another kind to encourage him to forsake the conviviality which brought him low. We had no way for him. All we could do was to tell him to pull himself together —and, perhaps, to pray. There were not even the few to pray together for him, to stand with him in the break with his tradition. If God had a way, did He not need His Church to be the flesh and blood of it? If we were not repenting for what we were as a community, how could we help this man to repent of what he had learned from the community?

I stood sometimes in these days at the Herd's Point, on my way back over the hills from the Glenconnar shepherds, with the whole of Crainie stretching below me, turning it over in the eye as the buzzards did. I could tell, field by field, how the farm work was in hand—the grey cloud of gulls at the Haugh the sign that they were still at the ploughing of their lea-land; the dust behind the horses at Northfield, indicating that they were already harrowing; the curl of smoke at Bridgend announcing that Tom Carruthers's wife was home from helping at one of the hill farms; and the gate still open at the school because the school car had had an urgent errand to the local hospital.

They came before me one by one, these people of Crainie, as I stood and thought of them; it was as if I were looking upon them from beyond time and space; and I loved them one by one. But how was I to do for them what my love wished?

When it came to the words to be spoken, the help given, within their daily life, in the moment of confusion and wrong, I did not seem to be able to do for them what they most needed.

5

DURING THE next two years Jen Pringle might have said often enough that her warning had come true: " Mark my words —ye'll be in an' oot o' trouble a' the time." The trouble was never far away, and in the end it flared up in the Kirk Session through a word spoken in anger against John Forsyth.

He had made the most of himself, as Crainie said, from the days when he had been helped by the old schoolmaster to go to High School and University. After some years in the city he had come back to the lawyer's office in Burnfoot. He had the learning; and people respected him for it. But perhaps there were other feelings too; and it was more than anger that leapt out at him in the taunt that he was a bit above himself—and his mother a " plain body " who had taken in folks' washing. It set something burning in him which was more than anger; and it burned against all of us.

When there was disagreement with anything he had said, he saw in it another man who was against him. Within the Kirk Session every proposal put forward by a laird put the fire into his face; and if the minister supported it he came under the same lash; he was showing himself a " Laird's man," in the pocket of the wealthy. Every issue in the parish raised the issues of the conflict in Forsyth himself. If someone was to be helped it was an insulting charity; if some work had been ill done, who were we to criticise it who had never laboured at that job with our own hands?

I tried to reason with him; but always he put up his defences. If I could not see the one simple fact that he had been sneered at and despised for the humbleness of his birth, if I thought there was any other side to it at all, then I was no better than the man who had spoken it.

But there was another side to it, not to the taunt but to what he was allowing it to do to him. The taunt had been evil; but there was evil in him which it had inflamed; and there was something to be said about that too. I had the right to speak; a greater name than ours was at stake; we were becoming a by-word in Crainie for our bickering. But I was speaking to a man who had a fire running in his mind; and I had not the power to stop it.

One night, at the end of a long altercation, two of the older men said they could not go on; they were broken by the quarrelling.

I walked up and down the road afterwards, trying to think how peace was to be restored amongst us, praying that John Forsyth might be forgiven for the hurt he was doing. As I turned in my walking I came within sight of his window; and I stopped, thinking of the man sitting there behind the drawn blinds. Something cried out in me because I had not been able to mend what was broken—like the cry of the disciples " Why could we not cast him out? "

In the cry I knew what I had never known before. I had often been praying for him; but I knew in the flash of that moment that, even in my prayer, I had been separated from him. I had been looking at his sin, and judging it, and asking that he might be forgiven. I had not been standing beside him, my sinfulness beside his sinfulness, asking that we might both be forgiven.

Christ had been seeking me too in this; and I had not

discerned Him. This was the Cross—His seeking, and my blindness and disobedience. This was the Cross—not far back in history but happening now in Crainie, because of me and for me.

The words from *The Diary of a Country Priest* were to come to me later: " Who are we to condemn another for sin? Our condemnation of his sin, our feeling of being removed from him because of it, makes us part of it; our condemnation and his sin are branches of the same tree."

As I stood there, watching that window, I knew that I had been brought there. What John Forsyth needed I needed. I was entirely one with him in it. It was not something he needed more or I needed less. I had suddenly understood the Cross as I had never understood it before. And the man whom God had chosen for me to stand beside for the opening of my eyes was the man who was destroying the work of my ministry by his opposition, and driving sleep from me by his accusations. Something in me had required that it should be this particular man and no other.

I knew now that I had been standing over against him, analysing the wrong in him, proving to myself why it was wrong, trying to show him how the wrong appeared to me, taking it out of his tormented life and holding it up before him to shame him and make him turn from it. Seeing him like that, I could not truly see the Cross, for all my preaching of it; and I could not forgive, for all my words of forgiveness.

I knew now that out of this moment the astonishing thing had happened: I had come to love this man who had angered and exasperated me; I had begun to see him as Christ was seeing him.

Was this, too, a sign of the Church as I had never understood it, for all my vows and preaching? Was this how we were to reach out to sinful men—by knowing that they were not more sinful than ourselves, by bringing them and ourselves under the same cry of penitence? If that was how we were to seek men it was more than " bringing them to church," to be within reach of the means of grace; more than going out to them to tell them of their need. It was to come with them within sound of Christ's cry " Father, forgive them." We had to be with them where they were, and as they were, so that we were standing with them in the same baptism, receiving for them as for ourselves what Christ has won for us by His Cross—not in the first place to urge the claims of the Church, or even to move their hearts, but simply to be where we belonged with them before Christ. That must mean the overcoming of many kinds of reluctance, the discovery of the right way to take ourselves to them, the right way to think about them, the right way for us to speak as men and women who had found that we were not better than others but that Christ had redeemed all.

How could we do it except by holding to men in their sinfulness and impenitence and ingratitude, allowing ourselves to be in the dust with them, to be of no reputation, to be maligned with them, to be despised with them?

This is the most difficult kind of poverty for the Church to embrace—so difficult that it has always seemed to some that physical poverty must be needed as a discipline in finding it.

I was seeing only a very little way. I had no strong courage for going farther; and I knew that, for the Church, no scheme of organisation could bring this about. But, wherever it was prayed for and received, it would be always reshaping the Church. It would keep disturbing it to its foundations and compel it to constant re-building, " removing those things that are shaken that those things which cannot be shaken may remain."

As I made my way slowly back to the manse I thought how I had been baptised into the Faith and had been surrounded all my life by the influence of Christian men and women; I had taken my vows; I had been for years dedicated to the ministry of the Church. Yet all these years Christ had been awaiting this hour.

What had He borne for me? On the Cross where He felt Himself lost to the Father, it was we who were lost. The Cross that He was still bearing for us told us again every day that we were lost, that we were all lost, that no one could look upon his brother and judge him to be more urgently in need of saving than himself. This was part of the mystery of the forgiveness which was in the Cross and in the miracles following. It was this that was being given me. I had never before said "Lord" within my heart and on my lips with this understanding of it, until I looked at John Forsyth's window.

When I reached my study I took up my Bible and read again how Saul of Tarsus, in a blinding flash, found Christ before him. For three days he had to sit in his lodging in the street called Straight, without inward or outward light, unable to grasp what had happened to him, praying that what had been begun might be completed. And Ananias came, the persecuted to the persecutor, " and, putting his hand upon him, said, Brother Saul."

I had been brought to that word. But I still had to wait, not three days but many months, while the hardness remained in John Forsyth's look and there was no sign of any new understanding in him. I was impatient for the miracle in him that had happened to me; and I may indeed have hindered it by my impatience. In him, too, Christ had to await His hour.

Only gradually did I begin to understand what it was that had happened to us. The deepest dilemma of human life and community had for us been resolved—the dilemma of how to condemn wrong without putting ourselves out of fellowship with the wrong-doer. It was this above all which frustrated the common life of Crainie. We judged and we separated. We took our stand on a moral principle, and made a cleavage between our brother and ourselves. Or we decided that we would not let it make any difference between us; and we contrived a community where moral principles did not greatly matter.

What John Forsyth and I had been given was the community which our community lacked—between two of us only, and yet the truth for the whole of Crainie; a small beginning for us, yet the earnest of all we needed to know.

This was the miracle of the Church. Only this Church could give the ordinary life of Crainie what men sought in it and could not find. This was how we were to become a new community within the ordinary community of men; not by judgment, nor by denunciation, but by being created new men and women together in Christ. This was the way of His peace.

6

FROM THAT evening, when I stood looking at John Forsyth's window, I began to see the Church in a new light.

The hardest thing for us to believe is often, in God's providence, linked to the plainest thing for us to do. He sets us down amongst the saints, to do the work of Christ; and we say "It is too high—I cannot attain unto it." But he leads us to a step so plain that every man knows that he should take it.

We are commanded to be perfect—with sinfulness still upon us. This is His word to us; and it seems unattainable. But there is also this other word following: "Jesus learned obedience by the things which He suffered"—the sins and sufferings of men which He made His own and took upon Himself to bear.

We cannot think of being perfect, even perfect in trust; but we can go to another man in his suffering and lift it to God as if it were our own; we can go to another man in his sin and ask God for common forgiveness as one in as great need as he.

I remembered a village priest in Provence who went to the waiting-room of the nearby railway junction every night when most people were in bed, because there the lonely gathered, men who had no home, men who could not face home because of what they had done, men who could not speak to any woman but a prostitute (because she had no pride left), men and women who were failures because of their own fault or somebody else's fault or nobody's fault. He knew Christ must be there; and he wished to be where Christ was, to make visible to these people the Christ whom they could not see, to take their suffering and their sin upon him, as Christ was, to pray for them, as Christ prayed. And this waiting-room became the place where Christ's priest was to be found, the *rendezvous* of rogues and those who had lost all respect for themselves and would never have thought to go where good people went. It became the church for them when they would not go to any church.

He became Christ's minister in the bearing of their sins and sufferings because he took the simple step to be in that place where he knew that sinning and suffering people gathered, and to pray for them.

I had visited John Forsyth with the wrong intention and prayed for him the wrong prayers; and yet, because I had known at least that I must be there with him and pray for him, my eyes had at last been opened, and I had been allowed to enter a little way into what Christ was bearing for him. What was beyond me to believe I was given to do, because I had not been altogether disobedient to the duty set before me, however blunderingly and mistakenly I had done it.

We cannot always know where this kind of sin and suffering is. But we can be where Christ has sought it out and will open our eyes to it. We can be where we know we are meant to be—where plainly there is suffering and wrong. We can take the first step to be the friend of sinners, as He was, simply by going to them, and being the most determined friend to the worst of them, going out of our way to be his friend, putting everything else aside and bearing any rebuff to be his friend.

One man's face came more and more compellingly before

me as I thought on these things. He had experienced what few in Crainie had known: a dramatic conversion. It had come to him through one of the narrower sects; and it was their influence which had moulded his new life. In judging his own past he seemed always to be judging other people who had had no such experience. He was scornful of the conventional Church, critical of the ways of its members. He gave people the impression that he had found the way of holiness and others had not, yet, for all his profession of what God's grace had done for him, he was still failing in the acts of charity and thoughtfulness which ordinary folk, who made no such profession, took for granted.

There was no one whom the people of the Kirk in Crainie would find it harder to reach. He did not want their sympathy. He would say he had " his own resources." What need had he of anything they could offer? They had no faith worthy of the name—so how could he want their help or their prayers?

There was no doubt about his suffering. In spite of his outward confidence he was a defeated man, straining to believe; a man on the edge of breakdown. What he still lacked was perhaps something which we had to supply, though we could not tell what it was or how it would come about. It might be that he without us could not be made perfect. That was the mystery of our sanctification: that we needed one another to bring us to holiness; and not only those who thought as we did and were easily congenial to us but those from whom we differed.

Could there be any doubt that, behind all that we resented in him, behind what repelled us, Christ was at work on him —however distorted the effects of it might seem? And could there be any doubt that He wanted some of us to be this man's friends, to go to him and break down the isolation, even if we did not know to begin with what more we were to do?

So long as I myself said of him " He has got his religion all wrong " I could be merely sorry for him or angry with him —and stay away. But when I said " He has got Christ's love for him wrong " I could not keep away. I was acknowledging that Christ was there. Could I be indifferent where Christ had set His love? I must be there to receive along with him, to learn along with him, to learn, it might be, from his error, but to learn as much also from my own; to be given grace along with him, however much he might seem at first to rebut me and be critical of me as a minister of a Church he considered to be failing in obedience; and, in the common receiving, at last perhaps be able to be the means of sharing his suffering and bringing nearer his healing.

But, as it was, we were leaving him to himself, except for the casual greeting on the road. We said he was going queer —we had seen before what happened when a man got " too religious." If he was suffering we did not suffer with him. It was a kind of suffering which took us out of our own depth. But we need not have thought that we were expected to plumb it, to solve the mystery of it, to produce our healing for the man's condition. We were to be where we could be used. We were to go and sit where this man sat, and await what Christ would show us. That was all.

I learned much from this failure, too, about the sinfulness of our divisions within the Church. It is not that we have different understanding of what the Lord requires of us, different temperaments, different experiences, different traditions. It is that we use these differences to prevent Him teaching us together, thwarting Him in giving to the one what the other lacks. Our refuting of this man's arguments was the symptom of our refusal to have fellowship with him.

It is always easier for us to say " Lord, Lord," to make an " act of faith " over and over again within the congenial circle of those who think as we do, in our own congregation and our own denomination, than to do the things which He says—to be willing to have God's Word come to us while we sit with the man whose theological system we have demolished, whose attack upon ours we have refuted. That, too, had to come home to us in Crainie through this man.

But it was a simple word first: to go to our brother while animosity was still upon us or upon him; to go, above all, where it seemed hopeless to go, to sit with him who gave us no welcome, to seek him out who had shut himself off.

" What good can we do ? " There was no plain answer. All that we could say was that we had prayed and put ourselves beside him—physically, obstinately, awaiting what God would do.

This is where we often turn back " and walk no more with Him," because this is the Kingdom and we are in it before we are ready for it. We are being bidden to do things which seem beyond us: to hold to the truth as we have seen it, and yet be ready to learn new truth through fellowship with the man whom we believe to be in error; to accept an obedience to which others may be blind, without despising them, without feeling holier than they. We must be prepared to fail. We must often learn by failing, because this is how we are to be humbled to be brothers in our need when we will not be brothers on any other terms.

7

But how were we to learn to love our neighbour as ourselves when to love him seemed to go not only against our own interests but against the interests of the whole community? That was the question Crainie was soon to be compelled to meet.

" Whosesoever sins ye remit," Christ had said, " they shall be remitted unto them; and whosesoever sins ye retain they shall be retained." It was not a commission to priests; it was a word to the whole people of God. We were binding and loosing every day in Crainie, with little understanding sometimes of what we did.

John Purdie had been a ploughman at Mortimer's and had given way one night to the temptation of an open window in the village . . . and there was suspicion that this was not an isolated theft.

I found him on the day of his discharge from prison in the derelict cottage a few miles out of the parish where his wife and family had been living while he was serving his sentence. I had better news for him than he could have expected. David Sim of the Brae was willing to take him on.

Purdie was incredulous. " He must ken," he said.

I told him that Sim not only knew but was offering the place because he knew.

" But . . . could I come back? "

Till the night before I should have said No. But if any man could put Purdie on his feet again it was David Sim.

By the time they arrived at the Brae the parish had heard the news and begun to speak its mind. A burglar had been deliberately brought back amongst them. He would soon be at his old ways again. The folks living alone would never go easy-minded to their beds; and there would be a run on burglar-catches in the ironmonger's in the town. Only a few spoke to me; but I heard the opinion of many more from them. Giving a man another chance was maybe right enough —but not when it took away folks' peace of mind.

" David Sim'll rue the day," was Mortimer's verdict to me. " Mark my words he will."

I was sure he would not. He might have trouble with Purdie, but he would not turn back on what he had done.

" I was strict with him "; Mortimer granted; " but I was just—and that's how he paid me back." But I knew that justice would never redeem Purdie.

There was no mistaking Crainie's attitude, in spite of the respect for David Sim. They had Purdie labelled. That was only to be expected. But was there no other voice in Crainie? Was it for the minister alone to speak the word of forgiveness, to declare from the Book that in the very place where it has been said that we are not God's people, there we shall be called the sons of the living God . . . in the very place? I was not a priest, to be left alone with the remitting of this man's sin. I was minister of the Christian community which had the retaining or remitting of the sin in their power.

But where were they to be found, thinking and praying about Purdie together—a company of people willing to take this upon themselves and lift it out of the ruck of ordinary judgments and opinions and bring it to God with their minds open to what He would reveal? If there had been a few, even a " remnant," together in one place, knowing their own sin and seeking what they were to do for their erring brother, ready to receive him again by the simple act of going to sit at his fire beside him, as Ananias went along the street called Straight to say " Brother Saul " to him who had made the Church suffer, there would have been some loosening of the man from his past.

This was not for the congregation on a Sunday; it was for a company of people small enough in number to be honest before each other and before God, and willing to take up their cross.

Purdie was being bound to his sin; he was being made to believe that he could never break away from what had happened; that this was the kind of man he was in the eyes of other people. If people thought of him that way, he did not need to care what else he did. And he was being made to think like this by the " people of God " in Crainie. We were to be the means of his deliverance; and we were binding him more closely. We were to be the means of bringing him where he could be redeemed from the destruction which threatened him; and we were thrusting him farther into it.

And there was Telfer of Kingleknowe. I wondered for long what had soured the man and turned him to spitefulness. He had had some strange misdemeanours in his youth which had the plain motive of doing hurt to the innocent.

His wife must have heard of the stories; but, if she had, they were never mentioned; they were thrust to the back of her mind. She may have wondered why he was accused of prowling about the fields and farm-closes at night with no good intent; but it was part of her determination to make the best of a bad job that she asked no questions.

It seemed too late in the day to do anything about his twisted nature; but if a man can be too old for the grace of God to make him new, it is not a saving grace—if too old, why not also too far gone in sin, beyond the reach of the saving power?

No opportunity was given me for a long time. Then one day, when I was talking with his wife alone, I saw suddenly in her look something more terrible than resignation to the inevitable. She had taken him with his faults, things she had not known, some of them, till after their marriage; and she had to put up with his faults, whatever compensation there may have been that no outsider would know. She had made up her mind to " thole " what could be not altered. Jacob Telfer was what he was and she was bound to him. What could not be mended had either to lead to angry words day in and day out, or to no words at all. She had chosen silence. But her silence was the retaining of his sin, her acceptance that there was nothing to be done about it by God or man. And I had gone often to Kingleknowe Farm, bought their eggs, discussed their crops, and returned home to my tea not knowing that in that house Satan had been desiring to have them and I had been letting him work unhindered.

I saw it suddenly as Christ must have been seeing it. I knew that He was striving for their deliverance. He was needing human words with which to break through to them, human acts to bring them where they could be delivered; and the words and the acts had not been there.

This was not something I should never see again. The evil had been retained until it had grown monstrous—that was all. We turned away from it and were thankful to put it out of our minds. But it was no more than the common sin of man, become abnormal and hideous.

In an earlier day in Crainie they would have said that Telfer was under the demons, and they would have linked the evil in him with the evil out beyond him. We called it his character, the way he was made; and we let his wife be thrust out alone, within the isolation of bedroom and farm parlour, to meet the evil and to come to some sort of terms with it. She had asked for it, we said, in marrying Telfer—she must have been " hard up for a man." And with that she was left to him, left to create a callousness towards him which was not in her nature— and to an escape in the daily chores of the farm-house.

What could the Church of Christ in Crainie have done? If even two or three had been gathered together to pray for them, who had been married with the blessing of God through His Church, there might have been a way opened up. But there had been no two or three.

No doubt the minister of Crainie in that day had made his intercession for them; but who had continued in his intercession?

A man's sin had been retained by his wife's acceptance of it. His married life, which was to have been sacramental in the releasing of him from the evil that was in him, had become the means of enclosing him more completely in it; and the Church which was present to his marriage was absent from his home when most he needed its prayers. The people of God, committed with the power to bind and loose, had known nothing of their power. Jacob Telfer had been left alone to face life and eternity.

The answer might have come in ways that no one outside would ever have known, in the speaking of a stumbling word between Telfer and his wife which would have acknowledged that they were in the grip of something they could not deal with—instead of that hard silence.

But a word had been needed, too, from Christ's minister which had not been spoken, a word to tell them that this was not anything strange that had come upon them but what was common to man.

As I tried to help them now I marvelled at the kind of words that sufficed for faith: humble words that did not hold together, honest words that stumbled farther than they were meant to —sometimes a despair about words altogether which drove a man to blurt out what he had been holding back.

The first words that came to Jacob Telfer some weeks later were farm-house words. "I'll gie ye a haun' wi' the dishes, Mary," he said to his wife, who had never been helped with the dishes since they were married. No one overhearing them would have known that he was on the way to something he had denied himself, and been denied, since he was a boy.

8

THE TRUE light was shining; but it made all the darker some of the things which happened in our community. We were afraid of the love of God; and when we turned from it we seemed to put ourselves in the hands of the prince of darkness.

We had rid ourselves of many of our superstitions; but sometimes in past days the superstitions had come back because the Church had belittled the powers of darkness and spoken as if there were nothing to fear. The men who lit the Beltane fire knew that we had much to fear. We did not destroy the power of evil by pretending it was not there.

Something happened now in Crainie which made plain to me why the Crainie of former generations had gone to the Knowe—man, woman and child, the whole people for their cleansing all together.

When the ancient rites had been secretly revived in later centuries the Church had seen only a sinister return to paganism. But it was a judgment against itself that was there. The hearts of men were uneasy. They were acknowledging that the power threatening them was greater than the Church's preaching said. It could not be summed up in the faults and frailties of human nature. It was an enemy, a destroyer of life.

Christ had seen Satan desiring to have His disciples. He was " a man of His time " when He spoke like that in these words, the Church had said. But it had not said that, whatever the form of words, this was insight into evil, into its range, into its power, by the one whose mission it was to meet and to destroy evil.

I saw it like that, like a threatening enemy, when Peter Lockhart and his mother came from Glasgow amongst us. Peter's father had left them after a long time of strife and cruelty in the home; and the effects of it were in the boy's distrustful eyes and ill-nourished body. He could not do ordinary work because of a bad leg; the most he was able for was helping in the garden at Crainie House.

Everybody was sorry for him at first; but he had a bitter way of speaking, and no gratitude for what was done for him. Even before the thieving from the "big house" was discovered the first pity was being strained. There was a hardening against him. But the hardening was more than a feeling of anger for the abuse of the kindness he had received; it became a temptation, an argument that you had to be careful in the helping of people you didn't know, to be guarded in taking in the stranger. When it was known that he had been stealing the temptation grew stronger. They had been fools, people said, to take him on at Crainie House; once a lad began to go that way there was no trusting him with anything.

Almost the whole community was resentful that this boy, with the bad influence of the city upon him, should have come into their village. Man by man they closed their hearts to pity. The factor began to think he had been too generous in letting them have the house, a neighbour to regret that she had befriended them when they came. A farmer said that it showed once again how you never knew what sort of character you had working for you. I was afraid, myself, when I saw that compassion had not been justified.

It was, in unsuspected form, an assault upon our faith, as if an enemy had done this, seizing the chance to turn us a little farther away from the kingdom of God's love. We became more ready to argue that all that boys like that needed was firmer handling. It was the work of Satan. Peter had become an instrument of the powers of darkness.

A few weeks after this his mother, working beyond her strength in the digging of their garden, caught a chill from the cold of a spring evening. When pneumonia developed she had no reserves to bring into the fight and no heart to hold on. She had failed with Peter, as she had failed with his father; and there was no future to live for. The end was in sight from the beginning.

When I looked up after the prayer at the grave-side Peter was standing with bent back, shaken by a sudden burst of tears. As we turned away he jerked himself erect again and went ahead of me alone down the pathway to the gate. I saw that he was walking without any limp.

When we sat, a few hours later, beside the fire in the manse I asked about his leg, how it was suddenly so much better. It was plain from his look that he did not know he had been walking differently. He asked me if I thought he had been shamming. The tone of resentment was back; suspicion came into his eyes. It had never been in my mind; I knew how in a moment of sudden emotion we have the ability to do what we have never been able to do at ordinary times. But I had brought a new fear to him. His bewilderment and anger made me wonder if I had been right. Before he left me I had become certain that, like the stammering of a child who has been unhappy and insecure in his home, Peter's lameness was more than a physical hurt.

I had spoken too soon and lost his confidence; I had exposed him to himself without preparing him for it. And

again it was Peter who paid for it. He disappeared the following week—back to the city where he could find obscurity and
be lost to the gaze of people who knew too much.

It was not the end of Peter's story for me; but it was the
end of it in the meantime for Crainie, except that it had
become easier to harden our hearts.

I was confirmed later in what I had guessed. Years before,
Peter had exaggerated a hurt until it settled on him and became
his escape from the harshness of his life and brought him
sympathy. And then something else in him had rebelled
against his limitation; and he hungered for excitement and
found it in the risks of wrong-doing.

We had not taken the trouble to try to understand him.
We had not been moved in heart to be near enough to him
to be shown the truth.

The first step was one that anyone in Crainie could have
taken, the physical first step in the direction of that house
where there was suffering and distress. In a curious way it was
perhaps because we were ourselves, like Peter, not facing
realities, that we held back, preferring the easy condemnation
to the difficult effort of being his friend—and yet the first step
was not difficult; it seemed so only because we were afraid of
where it might lead us.

The community of the Church should have been able to
take the strain of these experiences which the community in its
daily encounters seemed incapable of handling. We were the
people of God, the same people who gathered on Sunday as a
community in the Spirit, facing an evil in our community
during the week which we were powerless to overcome. We
who were the Church of Christ in Crainie, the Christ triumphant over sin, the Christ promising power, had no power to
understand and to overcome what Peter brought into our

midst. We sized up the circumstances as anyone might do, Christian or pagan, and came to our judgment, and argued our opinion against all-comers; but we never came, ourselves and the boy together, to Christ for His judgment and His mercy; even a few on behalf of all. We did not seem to need His word; we had already made up our minds; we were not even in much perplexity in making up our minds.

This was not the Church as He had created it. This was not the company of His people, earnestly seeking the way His love would show for the saving of a life, for the bringing in of one of His bewildered and broken and erring children into the family where he could be restored and healed and forgiven. We were the worshipping community on Sunday, and the hard-headed realistic community during the week; the same people, yet two people, ruled by different worlds.

For all our light-heartedness, our gaiety and our good fun, we were a community breaking down because it was trying to hold two incompatible principles within its life; but we would not learn the lesson of it.

We gave way to our fears about the evil outside us because we were afraid of the evil within. We were anxious about whatever seemed to threaten the peace and security of our community because we were clinging to the same kind of peace and security within ourselves. We feared, but we did not accept the deliverance which was at hand. Our fear was our sin. Where we had been told we were not to rest we were resting. The battlements which God would have away we were determined to build up and keep in repair. We would not let ourselves break down, as Peter for a moment had broken down, so that Christ might give us life. And it was a sign of it that, with Peter before us, we could only condemn; we could not stand with him; we could not stand him.

In *The Desert Fathers*, the records of the hermits in Egypt, a brother of the monastery is rebuked by the abbot for some wrong-doing and ordered to go from their company until he has come to a true penitence. As he walks slowly out, " Bessarion arises also and walks out with him, saying ' I too am a sinful man.' "

I had myself drawn the mercy of God when I had known my need to be the same as the need of him whom I condemned. I had known the urgent word being spoken to me; it had burst in upon my mind; it had caught me, arrested me. How could I doubt that the urgency I knew in it was the measure of my need? If I had any ministry at all it was a ministry created in me out of the very fire that had threatened to destroy me, and was still threatening.

9

" WE DINNA CHANGE," Jen Pringle had said of the Crainie folk. We counted on it that our neighbours would be the same mixture of kindliness and cantankerousness; that we could not rely on this man, that this other was always dependable. Someone might pull himself together after a lapse, it was true; but that was how you described it; he pulled himself together to be as he had been before; or he mended his ways and became as he had always had it in him to be.

But why did they change so little? As I learned to know the people of Crainie better I saw it was not because they were indifferent towards new things; it was much more because there was a certain kind of new thing which they feared.

One night, when I had gone up the glen to a shepherd's cottage, I found him sitting at his fireside with his daughter opposite him, unable to raise his eyes towards her for anger. He was ashamed of what had happened; but it was not shame only. He was holding on to some idea of right and wrong, because it was what he had lived by; and now it was keeping him apart from this girl when they needed each other most. He wanted to get up and put his arm round her shoulders as she sat there, bent over the fire; but something else in him made him determined not to do it. He was struggling against himself. It was not that he had been a man of such uprightness. He would not have said that he was condemning her and acquitting himself. He was trying to keep in check something he did not understand, some impulse to let himself go where he could not foresee—into a relationship where his old landmarks would no longer guide him. He had to stand by the right, he thought, the principles which had shored him up when he was unsteady himself—or he had to love and appear as if he were condoning what he knew to be wrong. He saw himself battling for the right; but in reality he was struggling to hold on to something in himself, what he had considered it reasonable that a man should be asked to be.

I knew suddenly, as I watched him, that this was why we did not change. We often did not want to be as God would have us be with our neighbour, or even with those we loved within our home. If we were to look for the root of our sin it was somewhere here that we must find it and not in the sins we could isolate and condemn.

He was on the edge of breaking down. That was his hope. He had to break down. The woman in adultery was once more before the Pharisee. This is our human predicament; this is the confusion we are in, that we can scarcely judge evil without increasing the evil in ourselves.

This is the key to the nature of our sin—why Christ has to break in, why He has to break down what is shutting us off from God and man.

I was afraid for this man, as he began to lose grip on himself—until I saw that it was his grip on himself which held him back from God and from what God wanted him to be.

I was on the instant ready to comfort him and bring him back to himself—until I saw that this was exactly where he must not be brought back. The evil was not in the crumbling of his life but in the shoring of it up, not in the suffering of mind which he was going through but in the desire to escape from the suffering.

As I watched him later, dazed by a new word which he could not yet understand, being led like a child where the understanding could break upon him, I marvelled that we are so slow of understanding who submit ourselves without fear to the surgeon's knife and will not submit ourselves to this surgery, who are in agony of loneliness because we have separated ourselves from our brethren and yet will not let the barriers between us be broken down. Our fears are for the wrong things—fear that our defences will fall down, when it is our defences which put us in peril; fear that we may have to be changed, when our wretchedness comes from going on as we are. Our affliction, which is " but for a moment," is magnified until we cannot see the glory that is to be revealed.

In a strange way this is true also for communities and nations. It was perhaps this that Karl Marx discerned afar off when he saw how nations, like individuals, hold contradictory principles within their system. The crisis and breakdown which they have to face is due, not so much to inefficiency and lack of control over their economic life, as to the attempt to base themselves on self-interest and all the while be seeking to establish institutions in their midst which refute self-interest as a basis for human community. We break down because we are attempting the impossibility of serving two masters. When we understand this the breakdown is no longer something to be staved off, but to be accepted as judgment. It tells us what we need to know, and do not like to face, about ourselves. The system is the reflection of the kind of humanity we have made for ourselves; and in turn we are the kind of men encouraged by the system—system and men interlocked, resisting the community to be.

It is nearer the truth about our condition than our easy assumption that we must found our community on self-regard but after that may add a superstructure of common interest and love for our neighbour. As with ourselves as individuals, we cannot treat the disease until we know whether breakdown is incidental to our condition or basic to it.

I saw a woman in breakdown because of a father's death and a brother's callousness. She had no one to turn to—she who had busied herself in the affairs of every second house in Crainie, who had rushed here and there with her advice when trouble overtook a family, who loved to be called in to set things to rights. She who was the friend of everybody had no friend.

I was afraid for her at first. She was on the edge of collapse. But there had been a woman by the well of Samaria who had had many to love her but knew herself unloved, and had given herself to loving but had never loved—left to fend for herself, finding her every task accentuating her solitariness. There had been a word for her because her pretences had collapsed and she had no one to turn to, though she had been the intimate of many.

I must no longer be afraid for this woman. She was coming to herself. She was throwing away the crutches with which she had been helping herself to get through life; the esteem, the flattery; and she was knowing herself for the first time as a cripple who had to be given the power to walk.

For what word had I been sent to her? Not for comfort as she expected comfort, but for the truth. There would be no shielding of her, in Christ's intention, from the truth. There would be no patching up of what should never have been built. She must understand what was collapsing—not herself, but the falsity she had been making of herself. She was there now, able to be spoken to as she had never been spoken to before, able to hear what she had been determined not to listen to.

Christ had come to me when I cried out in this very dilemma. I had to see hopelessness in others, too, as the moment when He could best speak to them. As the Father sent Him so He was sending me—not to give sympathy which heals the hurt slightly and leaves it festering beneath.

If we look for the kind of peace which will leave us as we are we shall find that it is not to bring that kind of peace that Christ has come but with a sword to pierce it. If we wish to be comforted and assured that, because there is forgiveness, we can rest in what we have made of ourselves, we shall encounter Him who will not let us rest.

This is something we have to learn together and alone, in the secret places of our life and as men and women learning to speak the truth to one another in love. The true Church is the fellowship of people in whom the old human life is breaking down and the new life in Christ is being formed. We must have understanding and nearness to encourage one another when the defences are crumbling and we are not yet sure of what is to come, when we are like the potter's vessel which must be broken and made again.

Was the Church bringing the people of Crainie through these experiences? Did we ever meet in such a way that these things could happen?

When we asked what the Church should be we must look for the beginnings of the answer there, where Christ was working the change in men and women for which He has come. We must find how to be with Him there, what He expects of us there, and ask how we are to be together for the doing of it. Our being together, the form of our fellowship, must be shaped by our preparing to be workers together with Him.

In the beginning the twelve returned and told how it had been with them when they went out on His seeking and saving, and were at once taught what they must henceforth be to one another.

We are not to be a settled company with established ways, shaped to a fixed pattern from which we fear to depart. We are to be a people of God perpetually giving new shape to our fellowship by what we are learning of Christ in His saving work.

The proof of it is that the family is the type of what the Church is to be, the indication of its form and character—the family, with its changing pattern where we learn new relationship in Christ and are knit together because of what He is doing with us and setting us to do.

Were we prepared to find our proof of it there in Crainie—in our homes, with the children; how we thought of them as they began to conform to the ways of the world, whether we feared for them in the right way, feared for the building up of a life which was on the world's foundations, feared when they began to make themselves secure against the unknown to which Christ was leading them, or feared instead for any trembling of the foundations which He was wishing to take away?

I watched them, these children of Crainie, searching for an understanding of the mysteries. I watched how soon some of them began to build their defences, to keep their darker thoughts to themselves, and to shut them away at the back of their minds, not to be spoken about or acknowledged; by their second year at school beginning to recognise evil in other children, deciding what they would do about it, looking around to see what older people did about it.

At five many of them had learned to look for their ways of escape from the difficult decision. By six or seven they could be finding how to shut themselves off at their play from the boys and girls they did not like; by ten pretending that they did not care; before they had qualified for the secondary school hiding their talents, burying their powers, learning, like the older people whom they were imitating, to evade what the Lord God was requiring of them, setting their defences against the demands of His Kingdom and adjusting themselves to the existing life of men—and being shaped by the evil to which they were accommodating themselves.

Even when we are children, if we accommodate ourselves to the world's evil we entrench it within; if we judge, we are judged; if we condemn we come under condemnation; if we harden our heart we are hardened against the mercy of God. Even as children, in the decisions of school and play, we come under the sway of man's sin.

When we passed these children on the road on their way home from school we spoke easily about how they were growing up, how young Jimmy was the very image of his father and would soon be taking his place behind a pair of horses, and Jenny would be having a home of her own in no time. We did not concern ourselves very much about the other thing that was happening to many of them: that they were already learning from the older people how to set the limits of their life, how to put a measuring line round it to decide what was reasonable and worthwhile and what was not; and, in taking their measuring line, setting the limit to what God could expect of them.

But there were homes where they were not allowed to

settle like this and shut themselves up in their defences. I was in a farmhouse one evening when a boy ran from the table, hurling himself from the room to get into isolation from an unkindness he had done, surrounding himself with the sullenness by which men protect themselves from recognising their sin—and then, without warning, coming back to the table and whispering to his mother that he was sorry.

He was not overcoming a childish temper or learning self-control. (He might achieve self-control only in order to safeguard his self-respect and his position with other people, while beneath the surface the same anger might be flaming unchecked.) He was being delivered, not only from the temper but from a deeper evil—the subtle adult ways of concealing that the temper was there, from adult sin as well as from childish tantrum.

It happened like that with him because he had been shown why he was made like this, and what went wrong. He had learned that the sensitiveness to hurt which put him under temptation to sulk was the same sensitiveness which made him fear hurt for other people, and that the zest which put his temper on a trigger-hold gave him the impulse to help people in need. If he did not learn these things at five he would learn the other: how to see that his temper did not get him into trouble, how to keep his anger in check or out of sight, how to adapt himself to the condition of being a man of anger and ill-temper; and, in gearing his will-power to handle it, becoming more and more resistant to a more radical change. This evil was not to be controlled but to be eradicated. It came out in that home by prayer—the kind of prayer in which a father and a mother confessed as well as asked, knowing that they themselves needed the deliverance which they were seeking for their child.

It was Christ's work which I saw in that boy. Christ, who had set a little child in the midst of sinful men, had been restoring to him the child-mind when it was in danger of being lost, giving him back his power to speak the simple words of the Kingdom when they were being overladen by the complicated language of human device and evasion. " I have been wrong " are the very words men cannot speak when they have become separated and are resisting the change which God wishes to make in them to bring them back.

The home is in this the pattern for the Church—where the Church learns what it is to be. The home is a frontier where Church and world meet, where men and women and little children face the world's sin in themselves and make decision what they will do about it.

In that farmhouse three people were discovering how Christ delivered them from sin; and, in discovering it, they were discovering what the Church of Christ ought to be, what manner of fellowship there should be within it so that the same deliverance may be wrought for men and women, wherever two or three are gathered together.

This home was no place of mere tolerance, the adjustment of one personality to another. It was a place where evil could come out, and hurt, and be brought by everyone together to Christ for His overcoming, where shame would not be driven underground to fester.

I learned there that the Christian family should have the marks of the world on it as well as the marks of Christ—the world being brought into the open and seen as it really is, the evil spirit coming out, and being openly shown. It should not be keeping up appearances. If it has no marks of shame it will have no marks of glory. This is where we are to see the signs of a spiritual warfare. This is where evil is to come out into the open and be vanquished. And this is how it should be with the Church. It is in the family of the Church that we should endure the humiliation, the hurt, the shame, until we are all cleansed; that we should be one in this sense, one in our disunity, our conflicts, our differences, that the world may believe. Our unity must be born in our shame, one towards another, within the " little Church " where men know one another face to face.

We are to expect to be " troubled on every side " . . . perplexed . . . persecuted . . . cast down—within the Church as well as beyond it, within the fellowship of those who take Christ's name as well as in the encounter with those who do not acknowledge Him. This is what we should look for the Church to be—not a company of good people, earnest in support of right causes, but a people troubled because they bear the treasure of the Kingdom in earthen vessels of human sinfulness, perplexed because they do not see clearly of themselves what they are to do, cast down because they long to see the Church glorious and triumphant, persecuted because men, even Christian men, will often hate what judges and rebukes them—yet not distressed, not in despair, not forsaken, not destroyed.

We were tested, in home and in Church, by the manner of our love for our children. So often we loved them, but did not know by ordinary love what was best for them. We could not save them by loving them. We might fumblingly tell them what manner of love the Father had for them; but the habits of the world would be stronger than our words and human affection would not deliver them.

We had to learn the love of God—not only to tell them about it but to live in it; we had to learn how Christ loves the children of men, how He makes Himself one with them,

how He bears with them, believes in them, hopes for them—
and then give ourselves to that kind of love for our children,
putting behind us all other love, the love that takes inordinate
pride in their doings, the love that protects at all costs, when it
should be strengthening them for the fight, the love that
conceals uncomfortable truth, the love that cannot bear to be
disappointed in them and is angry when it is let down—the
whole range of what can pass among us for parental affection;
all this is to be left behind and the other love is to be learned,
with its risks, its loss of dignity, its honesty which brings us
down to the level of learning ourselves, its sacrifice of ordinary
ambition, until we stand beside our children as seekers with
them, fellow-sinners being taught together of God, even
though at the same time we have to be their guides and
counsellors; and, by that cutting down of ourselves, becoming,
as we have been told we must be, like children ourselves, and
discovering that, when we do become like little children, we
are able at last to give them what all our adult wisdom cannot
give.

We are beginning then to love them as God loves them;
and their eyes will be opened, and they will know Him; and
their fears will be cast out because this is the perfect love which
casteth out fear. And they will lead us, even while they are
themselves being led into knowledge.

That was something I had never thought of in Crainie—
the ministry of every man and woman in whom the grace of
the Lord Jesus Christ had been at work.

I had looked at Jacob Telfer and his wife and prayed for their
deliverance from their sullen animosity—but not that their
finding of new life together would overflow in gladness into
the Church of God and be the means of opening other homes
in Crainie to a life they had never known.

I had prayed for John Purdie, that he might be given a chance to make a fresh start and be received with forgiveness by the people whom he had angered—but not that by the grace of a forgiven life he would turn many to righteousness.

My expectations had been only that men might be freed from their bonds; I had not looked for the freed men leading the Church in the freeing of others. I had been thankful to God for the first signs of a new peace in John Forsyth; but I had not been bold to pray that this man whose bitterness had divided the Church should be the instrument to teach us reconciliation where we had never ventured. I had been measuring my prayers, and measuring my ministry, by my own expectations; but the Gospel was the good news of a life bursting the bounds of all expectations, men and women given powers which no one could have anticipated, miraculously raised up at the very point of their weakness; the persecutor becoming apostle, the skulking betrayer become the boldness of the Church.

The signs of what Christ was doing amongst us might seem faint against the background of the Crainie which did not change, these men and women so predictable in their ways. It was a work done in secret in the heart of this man and that woman. I had no doubt of it when I saw it; but I had thought of it as a mystery of God's grace, to be known only to the receiver. I had kept it secret and had encouraged others to keep it secret. I had forgotten that Christ's work is also His word, and that it should be spoken by the man in whom it has been accomplished. I had seen myself ministering to the people of Crainie; I had not had the expectation that they might minister to one another and to me—that the man who had been given peace with God was the man to speak peace to the neighbour at war with himself, that the woman who had broken down because she had found that her whole life was a sham and a deception was the one to be the friend of those who were still deceiving themselves.

I was not the voice of the Lord alone for the people of Crainie. He had other voices which they would understand when they were not given to hearing mine.

When a farmer called his men together and told them there would be a new way of working from that day because he had been shown the kind of man he had been, Christ was speaking in words which I did not know, the language of the farm-close where men give and take the day's orders, put an edge on their tongues and set themselves against one another, the speech of the day's work where those who are meant to be bound together adjust themselves to being apart.

The Gospel must be preached—but I could not preach it alone; it must be preached where men work; and not just by the minister where they work but by the men themselves who work, the men who fall under the power of evil there, the men who sin there in speech and action. The man who has lived in bondage to the world's sin there must live the new life there. The man who has spoken in the old language there must speak the new there. The minister of Crainie cannot do that for him; it is his own word from the Lord; and it must be spoken to the men who will hear and understand that word and no other.

But the minister of Crainie could believe. There was one way by which he had been brought low. There was one word which had been spoken to him when the defences crumbled and the walls he had built for himself fell down. There would be another word and another way for every one of his people, and for their children. But there would be a word. That was the certainty. It might be turned aside; it might be disobeyed; but it would be spoken and it would be heard, if it were prayed for and looked for in faith. Where two or three agreed in this that they were asking it would be done for them. The walls of separation would be breached; the isolation would be ended.

IO

MEN SAID to me sometimes that they could not see God. Where were the signs of His presence? What could He be seen to be doing in Crainie?

There were many reasons why they could not see Him. One was the evil which we ourselves had created.

I remembered what David Sim of the Brae had suffered in past days at the hands of Jacob Telfer. He had told me how his farm had been molested; gates left open, letting the heifers stray on to the roads; rape seed sown broadcast in his garden; parts stolen from his binders which were difficult to replace; old scythe blades put into the standing corn and hay, so that the horses had taken fright and would scarcely face the field. For long they were at a loss to account for it. Sometimes they wondered if it was the children about the farm; or young boys from the town. But the scythe blades settled it; they were known to be Telfer's.

Telfer had nothing against him openly; there had been no disagreement. But he seemed to have his knife in him all the time.

He had had his knife in himself too. I had seen him in these former days sitting at his fireside, turning in his chair with irritation, one minute speaking evil against his neighbour, the next saying to me that if I knew what sort of man he was I would have him out of the Kirk. He had resisted everything I tried to do for him. And because he resisted the Church he had resisted what David Sim was; the quietness of the man had been rebuke to his own restlessness; the forgiving word had driven him into the torment of acknowledging what he had been determined not to acknowledge. I had seen, as Sim himself could not see, how there was something in him which the evil in Telfer wanted to damage; if he could not damage the man he could at least damage his gear. But all that was now past.

While there was that in men there must be a darkening of our minds and a trial of our faith. We could not see all things in subjection under Christ; we must see instead forgiveness often frustrated, love unrequited, sacrifice seemingly made in vain.

We wanted to see the hand of God at work in Crainie, the sure evidence of His presence; but there was something in us which obscured the very thing we were looking for and created more evidence for our doubts. We were not men and women with pure eyes; we were not yet free; and we were closely bound to other men who were not free. We obeyed the Spirit and forgave our brother; but our brother might not be of a mind to yield himself to forgiveness; and we were left to learn a deeper forgiveness, while there was the increasing evidence before us that it had not succeeded.

I understood from David Sim's forgiveness, working in the darkness of Jacob Telfer's mind, turning it at first to a greater violence of evil and to the deliberate hurting of what it knew to be good, why we often cannot see amongst us the un-mistakable evidence of God—signs which would make any of us believe. We cannot look upon God; we can only look upon what God is doing; and often we have to see, not so much what He is doing, but what it is causing men to do against Him. Our eyes are darkened because men turn against His forgiveness and pile new evil upon it to obscure it; and we see an accumulation of evil, and say we cannot see a sign of His redemption. There was no Providence visible on Calvary.

As I lived amongst the people of Crainie and learned a little of what lay behind the outward appearances, I knew how it was with our judgments. We saw a man kept by law and custom to a life which did not openly violate his neighbour's good; and we might call him neighbourly when he was only law-abiding. We saw him busy with the day's routine; and we might call him zealous when he was only self-seeking. We saw him a decent man; but we did not look on the heart where there might be evil which the outward decency concealed. We might believe in the travail of Christ for his soul; but he might still be at ease with himself; and we would have no evidence before us that the travail was there.

Sometimes we saw a man with the marks of conflict plainly upon him, the violence, the outburst of evil, the open harm done to his neighbour; and we judged that there were no signs of a saving work in his heart. Yet his violence and his lawlessness might be the sign that God had touched his heart; it might be the result of anger against himself, his turning against what he knew to be the life appointed for him, feared because he knew he was not fit for it. We saw only the marks of conflict, the rebellion, the defiance; we saw the label which the community, for its safety, had put on him. We did not see the marks of the hand of God laid upon him in judgment, the proof that he was loved of God. And he might still be hurrying into the Kingdom before us, as Christ said the publicans and harlots were hurrying before the righteous.

As there is endless complexity in our sinfulness so there must be in the providence which seeks us and saves us within it.

It is we who, by what we are, make the ways of God seem obscure.

The life in which we meet with other men conceals as well as reveals what God is doing. It draws our eyes constantly to the outward man and often hides God's judgment and mercy in the hidden man within. And sometimes good men make it harder for the struggling ones by talking as if there were no mystery at all. We can seldom see providence so plainly as to be undeniable. We have to learn what it is like for ourselves— how we have been held and let go, as a child is held and let go by his mother in learning to walk; how we have been allowed to stumble so that we could learn to stand; how we have fallen so that we could learn to rise—we have to know it in ourselves before we can understand why God seems to allow our neighbour to suffer and to fall. We have to know how He has guarded and exposed us—how He has permitted us to go on in evil intent and then has suddenly, in His chosen moment, shown us where we were going—before we can judge why another man seems to be left to go his own evil way without hindrance, as if there were no God. We must know how we have rebelled in anger, because He has been rebuking our hearts by His forgiveness, before we can begin to understand why our neighbour turns in unjustified anger against us. The anger is the evidence of God's presence, not its denial.

We have to bear the constant sight of unfulfilment: the unfulfilment deserved, as we say—men getting what they merit in punishment; and the unfulfilment undeserved—the girl with a mother's love in her and no child for her breast, and her sister with a baby nobody wanted, begotten by mistake. We see the frustration of good purposes, the wasted sacrifice, the forgiveness that bears no fruit; and we ask where God is, that He allows it; and we slip into thinking that it is all happening in spite of Him, whatever He does—that men's lives are being lived out under other laws.

We are perplexed as we look out on the world and cannot trace the hand of God in the march of events; and then we find a meaning unexpectedly in the world of our own home when in time of illness we are thrust into sudden need and those who come to our help turn out one by one to be themselves in need of help. The network of a providence appears before our eyes; we give in receiving; we have what we ourselves require in being ready to be the friend of another's need; and we cannot believe it possible except that we are under a Father's care. Whatever else is in our world this indubitably is in it.

But sometimes, before we believe it firmly, the evil day comes upon us, the darkest mystery of all in suffering and sorrow, and finds us unprepared.

It was like that when a boy very close to my heart died, after lying long months, alternating between recovery and relapse. He had been at the height of his medical career, with the mission field ahead of him, when he had been struck down. From two operations on the brain he had won his way back slowly to health, only to be cut down again to weakness. His father and mother had watched him for the last two months, knowing that his patience and determination were unavailing, and that the work to which he had dedicated himself would never be his.

When I visited them after he died the words of comfort would not come. I had to sit silent with them till the easy words were out of reach of my mind and I felt the questions beating upon me which were beating on them. Why was he guided to devote himself to a calling which he was never to fulfil? Why was the blessing of recovery given when recovery meant only the facing of ordeal all over again? Why was his agony prolonged when mercy might have cut it short? It might almost have seemed that the compassion which he had wished to show to suffering men had not been shown to him.

At last, as we sat there, it seemed that we must come back to the simple things, the things we could understand, and leave the things that were too high for us as we were then. We thought about his patience, how he had endured blow after blow without bitterness or complaint; and his thought-fulness for others which seemed to have taken possession of his mind just when we might have expected him to be concerned most about himself. And there was his gentleness. He had always been kind-hearted, but there was something new to it these last years. We had all seen it. It was as if he had been responding to a love greater than ours.

We looked at each other without saying the word. We were acknowledging that he had taken on the marks which we knew had only one origin. We were perplexed, not because God had not been there, but because He had, because we had seen the fruits of the Spirit in a body of death; and our minds had cried out that what was of God must not be cast away. The mystery lay heavily upon us; but it was the mystery of God dwelling with His people, not the mystery of their being forsaken. We could not find the reasons we wanted to find; we were still left with the life unfulfilled, the man with bless-ings in his hands seemingly at the mercy of the microbe. But we were perplexed because we believed; we were sore-hearted because we had become more tender-hearted; we suffered because we loved; and love is of God.

Perhaps it was he who had gone from us who was being used to bring us back to the simple things when our minds were tormented by the immensities. There was always so much that we could not understand. But if God had been with him, what else did we need to know? If God had been perfecting him, did we need to ask whether it was for life here or for a life beyond our present sight?

How much we had to learn from someone else belonging to Crainie, an old woman of ninety, not by nature " a patient body," finding during long months in bed in Burnfoot Hospital a patience which put Christ's peace in her face and hallowed the whole ward around her. This was not her nature; it was something given to her. It was not resignation to circumstances; it was a new trust in Christ, in His nearness. " I'm well off," she said to me. " It's what you have that counts, not what you haven't."

Lying there in her bed, unable to sit upright, almost blind and very deaf, she became the Church for every woman in the ward, shaming them in their complaining and their resentment against what had befallen them, sharing with them her trust that the presence of Christ and His sufficient grace were always stronger than anything the body could suffer. She was the Church; and, when I went to minister, it was I who received; and, as I went from bed to bed after hers, it was to see eyes lit up with faith because of her. She had found—what we learn with such difficulty—that, when other things were taken away from her, the greatest of all was given. Greater was He that was for her than anything that could be against her.

She was the Church—and how much she had to teach us about all that the Church should be—because she was becoming wholly submitted to Him. How could she want more out of life than that?

" I'll maybe be here when you come next time—or maybe I'll be gone "—to be in the body or out of the body, what did it matter? She had overcome the world. Death had no more dominion over her.

The life of Crainie might seem at the mercy of casual birth and casual circumstance and casual extinction. Taken at a glance there was no answer, no lightening of the mystery, no meaning in which the mind could rest. We see only a little way at a time and the sight of a suffering child can bring our eyes too close to see any way at all. But even for Jenny Copland, crying suddenly as she nursed her sister's unwanted child, something was being brought alive in her which would have its fulfilment. Somewhere there was a work prepared for her which was going to be hers, and able to be hers just because she had not allowed the longing in her to turn to bitterness and because the tenderness in her had become more tender for the long waiting. The denial of it here was the storing of it " for a life beyond life."

There had been times when I had had a sense of the nearness of this world unseen and those who had gone beyond my sight, when the very help given me was plainly to continue a work which they had it in their hearts to do and had not been able to accomplish.

I had known it after my father's death; and it had made clear to me my call to the ministry. I had known it when a good man had died and I found continued to me the same kind of impulse to go to unlikely places with help which he had put into my heart when the words could be spoken between us. I had heard words of warning and direction which I was sure were Christ's and none other's. I had felt at these moments a surging assurance that the unseen Kingdom was all around; and that this was the ultimate unshakable reality.

The Church has a triumphant faith at its heart, a chorus of angels and archangels in the heavenly places, the prayers of the saints around the throne, the Christ who was dead and is alive for evermore. But there must also be the faith which enables us to take one step in the dark, when grief overwhelms us and we cannot hear the distant triumph song.

Christ has His word for the darkened mind as well as for the mind suddenly come into the light that is ineffable and full of glory.

II

It was hard for us to see God, too, because we added up life in a sum of all that man did, and there seemed to be nothing left out which we had to account for, except the mystery of our beginning and our ending.

It had not been quite like this thirty years before in the days of Dr. Meldrum. He had been a man having authority, a determining voice in the parish council, in the school board, in the administration of the Burnfoot Hospital, as well as being interpreter of the Word of God and the pastor of his people. They respected him as a practical man, the only man in the parish versed in the ways of the lawyers, who could frame a will for them or advise them on their legal rights, and the only man with some medical knowledge who could act in emergencies until the doctor came.

The minister still had his place. He was the preacher of the Word, the remembrancer of things eternal, a friend and help in trouble. But no longer did he stand at the centre of affairs where men's living was won. They could not any longer have reckoned him a man with authority because they were not clear what his authority was, how the Word of God which he administered related to the farm " toun " and the market; how the Church, with all its talk of fellowship, had anything practical to say about the trade and finance and industry which held nations and community together. The decisive factors seemed to lie elsewhere.

The Church pointed them towards a better life, exhorted them, counselled them, warned them; but it had no evident power to make the crooked things of life straight. If the power was there it was hidden.

In spite of their inherited respect for the minister, many of them, though they might not have put the thought into words, must have regarded the ministry as the least practical of the professions. The doctor did actually heal. The teacher was necessary to train children to earn a living. The man of business created the means of livelihood. The minister was in the background, the preacher of ideals—though there would be a disturbing thought at times that this world of the unseen he talked about came closer than you had imagined.

One sign of the change that had taken place had been, until recently, the almost complete separation of the doctor's and the minister's work. In his day Dr. Meldrum would often be at the bedside of a sick man before the doctor from the town, his big hands laid on the sufferer's head in prayer and comfort. He would be there to advise until the doctor came, and many a night he would battle with the doctor for a man's life.

Now the patient in serious illness was swiftly diagnosed by the doctor and carried beyond both doctor and minister to the specialist in the hospital; and the minister paid his visit and said his prayer and bore the news of the patient's condition to his family. The mercy of a nation's care for its ailing folk was resulting in a separation of the minister of the more remote parish from the work of healing, and his withdrawal into the function of reassurer. The decisive factors in recovery seemed to lie elsewhere.

A link had been broken which had helped to keep in men's thoughts that their bodies and their souls belonged together; they had been helped in the past to see their life as it appeared under the circumstances of disease and disaster, and their life as it was to be accepted under the providence of God, as one single pattern: measurable and predictable under the eyes of scientific observation, yet entering also into the great mysteries of which the Church spoke. Sometimes they were hard to reconcile, these two ways of seeing life; but the old minister's voice and presence had kept Crainie folk from forgetting that there was the providence as well as the privation. The link might be tenuous; but the sight of the doctor and the minister making their way up the glen in the same gig had helped to hold the two worlds together in men's eyes. Now the minister seemed to be relegated to the function of keeping men in good heart.

It was a portent of what had everywhere been happening to the Church. The decisive factors in men's lives were appearing more and more to lie with the specialist politician and the specialist economist, with the scientist applying his knowledge for human good or ill, with the Government department, with the administrative heads of industry. It was a retreat from the fight—and at the very points where it had been said that by faith we would be more than conquerors: in tribulation, distress, famine, peril, sword . . . in distresses of body, in days of insecurity of the daily bread, under the sway of forces beyond our control, exposed to the threats of war. These were the very situations in which faith was to triumph; and the Church was the custodian of faith; and the Church was the fellowship of faith.

Dr. Meldrum had taken the affairs of the parish upon him because he had believed that there was no separation between the Lord's work and the daily work of men; where they worked He was at work. It was part of God's providence that every child should be helped to knowledge, for all knowledge belonged together, and that the community should order its affairs in council for the good of all, for all were under His providential care. The minister was not taking up extra duties in Board and Council; he believed he was following his Lord where his Lord's work had to be done.

Had we been abdicating—not by giving up our seats in Education Committee or in County Council but by abandoning men to find their own way in these difficult reaches of life, to find and hold to their faith where the pressures of the world were upon them and they had to come to daily decision? Were we not leaving them to make what meaning they could of their fortune and their mischance, the blows of fate and the evasion of them? And then, when they found no sign of God's providence, no proof of His care, we rounded on them from our pulpits as a secular-minded generation.

Some became embittered at how things had turned out for them; some became bored and went into ways of escape; some set before themselves ambitions which they were determined to achieve at any cost of strain of body and mind.

The sickness which came upon many of them had its beginnings just here, where we had so often abandoned them to the world, when we should have been standing together under its pressures. And the doctor had been left to make them whole.

But how was he to be expected to save a woman whose sickness had its origin in mental tension, because she thought it mockery that Providence had set in her heart a passionate love of children and then denied her the opportunity for it? How could people talk of Providence, she would ask, a God who provided, when He gave you a power and a gift and then deprived you of the possibility of using it?

The doctor could not go back to that day when she had been unable to see God and had turned to anger—yet it was there that the sickness had begun which he was called in to cure. It was from this anger that the tension of mind and body had come which had hurt many and now was working its havoc upon herself. Was it for him to set her right with God?

There had been another work in these past years which had not been done, made harder because her secret anger against God gave her an anger at His minister, sitting there saying smooth things which she could not believe, rebuking her for what she could not help. Somewhere, some day, perhaps a day long since past, there must have been a way still open for the word to break through—telling her that she should ask of God to find others who needed to be loved, in a world where so many never knew love. But the word had not been spoken; perhaps she had not wanted it to be spoken; perhaps the minister had been afraid of her anger and had kept silent. There may have been such an hour and she may have been allowed to turn from it, preserving the appearances of faith but with faith actually shrivelled within her.

The doctor could deal now only with some of the consequences. It was the people of God who ought to have been healing the hurt from which the trouble had come.

What reached the doctor as physical and mental breakdown had its origin often where misfortune had been rebelled against when it should have set a man or woman to find the grace sufficient for their need. Behind physical breakdown was the story of the kind of people we were; behind the asthma the anxiety of trying to hush up the birth of a daughter's illegitimate baby; only the shame of it felt—no seeking out, with the help of supporting friendship and prayer, what God would have a woman do when this had befallen her home; only concealment, escape, choking the news out of sight.

We sympathised; but often, because the Church had no

friendship ready, no one with the urgency of heart, we did not help the fallen to rise. We were sorry; but we did not help the blinded to see. We made them feel we understood how hard it was for them; but we did not enable them to find how God uses life's hardness to soften hearts. Our very sympathy— if that was all it was—could bind them to their unbelief, because it showed that the Christian, too, had no more to say than " How hard it is." We identified ourselves with the illness and not with the recovery. We habituated people to look for consolation when they should be looking for the power to overcóme.

There was a special temptation when the minister assumed with men and women of transparent goodness that what had befallen them could not shake their faith—and no door was opened for them to confess that they were shaken.

I had often found sanctuary where old Mrs. Plenderleith and her daughter lived; she with her smile that had the assurance of Heaven in it, and Mary who made her mother her sole care. A minister could talk there of the things nearest his heart. Faith answered faith. But he could forget that the way of faith can be the way of sacrifice, and sometimes the sacrifice leaves behind a hurt not healed.

I knew what Mary had given up to be there at her mother's side. She had accepted the sacrifice nobly and without self-pity—but she had hurt herself wrongly in making it.

Not until she lay ill, unresponsive to any drug, did I learn. One night, after she had asked me to say a prayer with her, on an impulse I laid my hands upon her head as I prayed. When I lifted them she was asleep—and she had not slept for several nights.

Neither she nor I spoke next day about it. I do not know what happens at such times, how much it is a power in the

hands, how much it is a power used by a greater power. What
it meant to Mary Plenderleith was not that she had found sleep
after being denied it, but that she suddenly in that sleep came
to herself and found herself able to speak to me about what she
had hidden even from herself for years. Somehow in that sleep
she was released from a struggle. The hurt that had been
healed slightly came open for new healing. Words which had
never been given their chance to come out poured out now in a
great rush of honesty.

It was a sign to me too. A psychiatrist might have given her
great help. He might have laid bare the causes of strain; he
might have sent her back, at rest within herself because she
knew what had been tormenting her, had faced it and set it
behind her.

But what if it were something which she should not set
behind her? What if she were meant to be the kind of person
she had suppressed when she bravely made her sacrifice?
Who was to help to bring her to another kind of fulfilment?

She might be suffering from tension because she was denying
the grace of God in her heart even in honestly seeking to do
what she believed to be right, thrusting something out of sight
in her which He wished to bring to fulfilment in a new way.

Was this kind of tension something from which we had to
come back to normality, or something from which we were
meant to go on to a greater depth of life and understanding
than the all-too-stable person knows? That was a question
which could not be left to the psychiatrist to answer alone.
It involved the fundamentals of the Christian life. It raised
the issues of the sinfulness of the ordinary life of men—
how we barricaded ourselves against the Spirit of God by our
normality, by our determination to hold by what was within
easy compass of attainment and to shut out the unpredict-

able to which God was calling us, because it might involve us in new and uncomfortable insights, in a heightened sensitiveness difficult at first to bear.

This was the very marrow of the experience of being ill-at-ease, broken-hearted, hungry and thirsty, persecuted, which the people of God were supposed to know. This was where they were to be expert and able to speak with authority. To them belonged the decisive factors in human life, if they were receiving the promised grace together—but not to them, sitting row by row in church on Sunday; to them only if they were also together where these things could happen. We could not expect to see God at work in Crainie unless we gave Him the workers.

12

WE HAD to learn to see God where we worked—and that was often where we found least sign of Him, even we who laboured in the fields under the great hills.

We knew what the earth could bring forth, and what could go wrong with it, how it had to be fed and kept in heart and given the right rotation of crops. We had it measured so that there was no mystery left in it. But we could not understand this earth unless we knew for what purpose God had made it and what He had brought out of it. Always with the renewal of the earth there was renewal of what now went with the earth, what Christ had won for us on this earth.

Each day was a gift; the gift of life and the gift also of the grace for the day's life. The renewal of the day was the renewal of Christ's work as well as ours. The roadmen with their tools on their shoulders, the ploughman sitting astride his horse, the postman with his lamp at work on the early sorting of the letters, the housewife at the embers of last night's fire, were the reminders of more than Crainie's work beginning again in the new day; they said to us that this other work went on too.

The renewal of the earth was more than the promise of seed-time and harvest; it was the promise of all that Christ had won for mankind. The torment in creation, the convulsion that had made the Crainie hills and torn open the way for the rushing waters in Crainie glen, had given us the grains of soil on which we grew our food; and the torment on the Cross had given us what our hearts hungered for and could not find.

That the world continued at all was our assurance that the work of Christ went on. The new life in the fields, which made us decide it was time for the cattle to be out, brought with it the certainty that time was still being given Him to complete His work, that what He had won for us all together was still being won for us, man by man—won or lost by words as ordinary as the crops we handled, and sometimes as little understood.

The schoolmaster all but turned one man away from it by a casual word. At the first Sacrament after his appointment he was surprised to see his predecessor sitting in the church not far from the schoolhouse pew; at the next Sacrament he was there again, in the churchyard, surrounded by his friends. The new schoolmaster had made one mistake himself when he came to Crainie, and the churchyard was none too easy a place for him just then. He could not tell who would stop and speak to him and who would hurry by with a nod. Walter Brodie seemed to be making it harder for him, holding on like that to his popularity. But by the grace of God the schoolmaster said nothing.

Brodie had a reason which none of us knew. I discovered it long after. In his last year in Crainie he had a bitter quarrel, the kind of quarrel which seemed to offer no way out. He could never forgive the man who had done him the hurt; it would be with him to his dying day.

When he had gone from Crainie it continued to disturb him. Whether it was the hurt, or his inability to forgive the hurt, it gave him no peace. He could not forgive him; but perhaps, if he sat behind him at Communion and watched him take the bread and the cup into his hands and took the same bread and cup into his own hands, he might have better thoughts. So he came back, seeking the grace to forgive.

If a word of what had been in the new schoolmaster's mind had been spoken there would have been an end to the impulse. The voice of the Spirit would have been silenced. The hardness in Brodie would have grown harder. So narrow are the edges along which we walk; so easily are we turned from the way God is showing us. A hand on a door, held a moment longer than is necessary, may be all the sign we have of a man's impulse to say what he has been holding back for years.

Once, when I was coming away from a christening tea, I found that the father had mislaid the registration paper. As we walked to the car I said that I would call in for it during the week. " I'll bring it," he replied decisively, as he held the door open for me. " There's no need," I said: " I'll be passing." " I'll bring it," he said with finality, and shut the door before I could speak again.

Something in that sudden determination kept me from going to the cottage during the next few days. If I had gone and he had lost his excuse for coming to the manse I might never have heard what he had made up his mind to say as he stood with his hand on the car door, with the emotion on him of holding his first baby and hearing the words of the Church's prayer for him. There was a roughness of speech in him, sometimes bantering, when he spoke to his wife with other people present, sometimes a roughness more serious when he talked scornfully before the youngsters of the village. I had never before seen in it a fear of something in himself, the emotions that were more like a woman's temperament than a man's.

The vows he had spoken at the Baptism made him suddenly

wonder why he was ashamed. The moment at the car door brought the impulse to lay it all open. I should perhaps have been prepared after seeing his tears as he stood below me at the font.

If it had passed from him it might never have returned. His wife might have found him growing still less understanding, less patient towards her; and their boy might have grown up to sit with them at a table where only casual talk was heard, and much of it harsh judgment against the neighbours. Christ's Spirit would have come again. There would have been other moments of wondering, and perhaps a determination to win clear of the wondering. But one impulse of the Spirit thwarted and regretted sets the mind against the next; and a man may have passed the decisive moment without being aware of it.

It is not by the minister's word that the issues are decided; but it may be by his faithfulness to his Master's word in the unlikely moments when men and women make their opportunity to speak what is on their minds: the ploughman at the end of the furrow, saying that his horses need a rest, and holding the minister until he gets the talk where he wants it; the girl coming to the vestry door with a shilling for some fund, so intent on a chance to speak about something else that she goes off with the coin still clutched inside her glove; the farmer, heavy with a sense of guilt, coming to the manse to have an agricultural paper signed which has never needed the minister's signature before, standing there with his gift—a jar of honey for the release of his soul; a farmer's wife wanting the minister to come in though she is busy, wanting him in because she is busy and can tell him as she turns her scones and attends to the girdle what cannot be told face to face.

The conflict which shakes heaven and earth is for the

people of Crainie a conflict coming upon them while they mend harness, while they talk across the march-fence with their neighbour about a straying stirk. We are bound together in the little things—that is part of our providence—and in the little things we have to find our way to the Kingdom.

For one man in Crainie the way to forgiveness was opened up by his bees. On a Sunday morning they were nowhere to be found. Every garden in the village was searched; but the bees had gone farther. At last there came word that they had swarmed at the croft of a man with whom he had not been on speaking terms for months. Before the ten o'clock church bell they had to be reconciled, and not by any word spoken which mended their quarrel, but by the fetching of a ladder, and the holding of a sheet, and the words passed up and down as they saved the swarm in the gean tree.

There was an old woman in Crainie who found her way to reconciliation when she threaded a needle and set it on the garden trellis between her cottage and the cottage next door, so that her neighbour, unable to thread a needle for herself, could find it and know that all was forgiven.

It was in the little things, often, that men were able to make their peace and find their way back to God.

In the manse study I had a place where the touch of my hand on a Bible of special memories recalled me to the mercy-seat and spoke of my deliverance in past days. I had another place where at the end of each day I was reminded that I could not go to rest without the confession of what had been ill done, and stained in the doing, because of what I was.

We have had too much scorn in Crainie for the humble things which can be sacraments of the highest. We feared what the Church of Rome had done to us. By the touch of water men have been recalled to their Baptism, and by the

touch of bread made to see the Cross of their redemption . . .
until the very touch has seemed to have magic power; and
truth has been corrupted; and what was given to be our
remembrancer has become an idol and we have had to throw
it away. But we have lost, too, some of our understanding of
how Jesus took the homely things and made them the instruments of God's miracle.

I had the great word of the Gospel for these people on the
Sunday; but faith in the great word had to be found at the
garden fence and the cottage door, in the words and actions of
the day's work.

Alex Fleming's wife had never given much thought to
what might be happening below the surface of life. She had
her long day's work to do; and it filled her mind until it was
time to sleep. Her thoughts were mostly on what she was
doing with her hands—until she fell critically ill, and lay in the
Burnfoot Hospital week after week, while life ebbed and came
again like the breath on her lips. She scarcely looked up when I
went to her and prayed beside her bed. But one day there
was something new in her face; a new kind of life, a thankfulness and a shyness I had never seen in her before, as she held
out her hand to me from the bedclothes.

"I'm glad you've come to-day," she said. " I've just been
told. The doctor says I've got the turn and I'll soon be just as
I always was. But I could never be just as I always was after
this."

She was not going to let the moment slip by. My words
were not needed for her prayer; it was in her heart already
and would have been heard without words of mine. But the
putting of it into words made it a vow before man and God;
and that was what she wanted. It was the beginning of a new
home in Kildrochat, with time for words that had never been

spoken and quietness that had never seemed possible. Like the old schoolmaster and the young ploughman, she had known, although she could not have said what it was she knew, that the prayer of faith had been at work upon her, the prayer of the Church. She knew she had been remembered in the prayers of the people on the Sundays. She knew that there was a promise of blessing for the earnest prayer of those who were gathered together in Christ's name.

There was mystery in the Church—more mystery than we sometimes allowed for. It looked ordinary, like the earth we lived by; it could be seen as little more than an audience of people listening to a minister. But something else always seemed to be breaking through.

Walter Brodie had come back to his Communion because he felt that his heart would be softened and his hatred towards a man loosened. But it was the prayer of the Church that he was counting on, although he might not know it, the prayer of the Church, gathered around Christ's Table, for each man there in his hidden need.

Tom Smith had been taken by surprise, standing at the font, as it suddenly came to him that he was being prayed for by the people around him. But it was not his surprise that made him determined to speak to the minister about the things in himself he was becoming afraid of; it was the prayer of the Church preparing the way of the Lord, making an opening in his solitariness.

What we were to one another in the ordinary day's course could be the fulfilment of the prayer of the Church—as it had been with these people and me.

13

THESE IMPULSES, so insignificant yet so decisive, came out of the heart of us where we willed to do good but evil was present with us. Within us, deeper than we could search with our understanding, was the place of conflict and contradiction, where we were threatened by the power of evil and could be delivered by an impulse of faith as small as a grain of mustard seed. It was then God spoke.

It was when I saw how I was under pressure of evil in my praying that I began to know what must be there in the depths.

I gave thanks for my blessings; but usually it was a thanksgiving for what had turned out well for me, for the smoothing of my path, for the overcoming of obstacles. I confessed what I knew to have been wrong; but it was I who was confessing in order that I should be put right and at peace with God, not that He should be given what I had been denying Him. I said my prayers for other people; but often it was my asking for what I felt they needed, what I had decided would be right and good for them—what I wished, what I thought, was the centre of my praying. And sometimes there was a shadow of that dark evil, the thankfulness that I at least had confessed my sin and was not as the Pharisee. I at least had struck my breast and said " God be merciful to me, a sinner."

Right at the very heart of me, where I had assumed that I

was being honest before God, I began to see how deep were the roots of the self that seeks its own good; this evil from which I must be delivered there, in the very core of my being.

I began to see—or was shown. Just where it was darkest the light had to break, had to be turned upon me so that I could see myself. The day of another opening of my eyes was coming near.

Was that where the battle had to be fought out? Was that where the cross had to be taken up? I had not been prepared to give God time for that there—time to turn the light on me, time to turn me from myself and all that I was saying and thinking, to what He was thinking about me and for me.

This was where I had to begin to learn to deny myself—by allowing Him to speak, to correct, rebuke, change my mind. If not there, where I was most myself, how was I likely to learn to deny myself out in the pressure of meeting with other men, where I felt I had to stand to my own defence and argue my rightness? This taking up of the cross would never be understood out there in the heat of the moment unless I was learning what it meant in the quiet where I could be shown what I was not yet willing to see.

We are always under threat where we have to come to terms with those who acknowledge no obligation to Christ; but the threat is not so much from them, from the evil in them, as from the temptation it gives to the evil in ourselves; it is from this that Christ must deliver us. It is our own self-love that must be crucified; we cannot blame others. It is there at the heart of us that we must learn to turn away from ourselves and the concern about what we feel and suffer, what we think and wish to do.

Because we have not faced what we are there, at the centre, we are unready for the temptations, unsure when we are standing for the right and when it is only for our rights; and in consequence we do not know how to help one another in the crucial issues of our life. We hinder; we inflame men's desire for self-esteem when we should be helping to quench it; we expect them to be roused to anger because they have been slighted, when we should be looking to them to overcome evil with good; we appeal to their self-interest when we should be taking the appeal to a higher court.

We cannot help them in the taking up of their cross unless we are taking up our own. We cannot pray for them aright unless we have learned aright what to pray for in ourselves. We cannot strengthen them except by the sharing of the strength which has been given us for our own weakness. We have to help them to stand fast, not in the assertion of themselves but in acceptance of what Christ is doing for them. We have to help them to bear the cost of being seen to be new men, of being different from what they have been until now—of learning new ambitions, different ways of dealing with their neighbours.

We do not stand together now in these things as they used to in the old days. We do not speak so easily of what threatens and burdens us, nor of the way we have come to our convictions. The men before us had needed many a time to make decisions which turned them from their homes. But in making them they had been given the great blessing of seeing all lesser decisions in a clearer light.

Their testimony had come down to us, in their own words, written from one to another for mutual strengthening; the testimony of how they had been beset in these farm-closes by the assault of temptation in the confusions of their time—how they had been given the power to discern the true and the false; how they had been delivered.

Scotland was threatened by new forces as the atomic age came upon us; and within a few years the men who were struggling against poverty in the farm cottages were to be tempted in ways they could never have anticipated by an uprush in wages and the power to extend the range of their pleasures which the new money was to bring—and many of them were unprepared for the decisions which were thrust upon them. Even in Crainie this kind of change was upon us; and the world outside, with its obsession that the increase of goods was the chief end of man, would not let us be. We had to be told to produce more so that we might survive as a nation; and we were given the incentive that, if we produced more, we should have more to enjoy—till the whole people became inflamed with the kind of thoughts which had formerly belonged to the rich man seeking increase of riches.

The homes of Crainie were no longer threatened by these powers which openly over-rode men's consciences and seemed bent on taking away the supports of their faith; but they were threatened, as they had never before been threatened, by words from outside, words that many of them would never have heard a few years back, the power of the world's unbelief pouring in upon them and beating upon their minds. The words of other minds were there too, words of faith which lifted up the eyes to the things of God; but they were a still small voice in all the stridence; and many folk in Crainie were bewildered and unsure and in far greater danger of losing the supports of their faith than when Anthony Murray roused the parish because men from outside were taking away the means of grace by which his people had been fed.

We no longer gathered ourselves as men used to gather then, kneeling on the earth-floors of their kitchens to find in their perplexity what God would have them to do—and we needed it as much as they. We were gathered, Sunday by Sunday, in the kirk which these men had known; but we did not bring to the kirk what they had learned on their knees, neighbour with neighbour, in their own homes; and we did not take from the kirk what made them bind themselves together for the days ahead.

The men of a nearby parish stood alone, unprepared, when a sudden decision was thrust upon them and they heard nothing more than a call to make up their minds about a point of farming efficiency.

They were in the village hall, discussing whether a hostel for the farm boys should be opened in their village. It was not the decision about the hostel that mattered most—there could be fair enough arguments either way; it was the shaping of the attitude between employer and employed.

There was plenty at that time to draw the boys away to the cities—poor wages and bothies to live in which were often cheerless places—nowhere to sit except the bed, nothing to relieve the drabness; rats everywhere, so that all their belongings had to be hung up high or kept in the big wooden chest.

I knew how some of the bothy boys of Crainie, before their club was formed, had been driven in the winter evenings to loiter at the bridge-end because there was nothing for them to do, getting into trouble when they made an adventure for themselves, searching for some bit of life that would excite their emotions and finding it often at the expense of the girl in the kitchen.

The argument swung this way and that—" You'll lose your grip on them—they'll no' be to haud or to bind "; " We'll not get the work out o' them "; the voice of pity—" It's the halflins wi' nae hame we should be mindin' "—and the voice of shrewd speculation—" It'll give us men who will bide."

On that narrow edge of decision they swayed to their conflicting emotions. There might be something in it—it might give them more settled men . . . But still there might be less grip on them and the work might suffer. And then maybe a doubt about something that had been said—an echo from the Bible—but this had to be decided by whether it would work—and how could the Bible tell them that?

The minister of the parish was not there. He would be called in later, if the scheme went on, to do what he could for the boys and to say Sunday prayers with them. But the Church was there. Every one of them was a member of the Church; some of them were elders of the Church. But there was no voice of the Church there, with this decision on them and the voice of the Deceiver there, urging them " Would it work, would it work, would it benefit them, would it serve their interests? "

But it was not for the minister to be the voice of the Church, even if he had been there. He might have said that there were some things they were forgetting—but they were not forgetting them; they were only deciding what was workable and what was not. It was some of those men who needed to be the voice of the Church, putting what seemed workable in its proper place with what was commanded. Some of them should have been prepared, in the only way Christian men can be prepared. Even if they had been only a few they might have been given a word to speak which would have been a light to that company, swaying along on its edge of decision. The Bible, the Kirk, might have something to say later to their conscience; but it was now, this very evening, that the decision was upon them like a thief in the night; it was now that they had to be ready to take up their cross, to put a check on their own interests.

They were debating the possible value of a hostel; but it

was the value of human lives that was being weighed in the balance—how they were to think of these boys brought under their care, what they were to do for them on their farms, especially when they were stubborn and ill to handle, even if the hostel should be impracticable. This was the hour for the word that they were their brother's keeper, the hour to ask what that meant in the bothies of that parish. But it was not spoken. Christ was an idealist—that night they had to be practical men. There was no thought in their minds that He knew more about the ordering of a farm, and the dealings of one man with another on a farm, than they did.

It was the same way on Sunday mornings when Adam Baillie and John Forsyth made their separate ways up the path to Crainie Kirk; each, if he caught sight of the other, regarding him as an adversary. To Forsyth the Colonel stood for a social system which had created the poverty and degradation of last century, from which we were only slowly raising ourselves: a system which had given men political democracy while continuing to hold them in economic bondage; a system which had been partially humanised only as a result of long struggle and sacrifice. Forsyth knew that the Colonel was a just man with his employees and a good friend of their families; but he was involved in the defence of a social order which had been unjust and was still heavily weighted against many.

" I can't see," he would say to me, " how the Church can be true to itself if it doesn't speak out. We're Christians because we believe that Christ came to save us from our sin. Isn't it the business of the nation to save men from the effects of the sin? We can't make men moral by law; but we ought to see that men aren't allowed to work their sin into the life of the community and send it down to the people who come after them. That's what the Colonel's defending. And you're defending it when you're not attacking it."

And Adam Baillie would say to me of Forsyth: "John's good-hearted; but he's a spreader of trouble; he's poisoning the minds of these younger boys. They've no idea of doing a decent day's work for a decent day's wage."

They came to the House of God, these two, not just differing in politics but doubting each other's integrity; they sat down together to listen to the Word which should have made them one in their common need; and they said together "Forgive us . . . as we forgive"—and they went out again down the path thinking of each other exactly as they had when they came in and exactly as they had done now for years. There was no meeting-place for them where they could learn to differ with Christian understanding and learn in their differing a greater truth than either had yet seen. Politics was their point of separation, where they were driven into passing judgment on each other and condemning each other—yet the issues of politics were the issues of the sharing of God's bread, the caring for the needy, the bearing of other people's burdens, the restraining of the wrong-doer's evil, the redeeming of the criminal, the setting of the best life before the child. What should have brought them together as Christian men, even with their differences and tensions, was shutting them off from each other; and just there the Church was doing nothing for them; and the minister was moving with too easy a mind from the one to the other, perhaps a little self-satisfied that he could be a friend to both.

This was where they had to meet, at the point of their difference—not so that one might convert the other to his way of politics but that they might both learn to meet as Christians over the issues of human need, and to differ, if need be, in love. If we could not meet like that we were placing a taboo on politics whenever we were together in Christian circles, deciding to leave the issues of men's common life outside the region of Christian action; and unreality had at once entered our fellowship; it could not stand the strain; it could continue only by withdrawing from the conflicts of ordinary life.

In the beginnings it was because men met at this level of fellowship that they were emboldened, in spite of their Roman citizenship, to say that they must obey God rather than men.

We were not a fellowship of the Spirit until we were brought together at the very point where we differed on issues fundamental to the Faith. This was one way of taking up the cross. We had to accept the division that was there in us; we had to work within it as citizens fulfilling our duty; yet we had to be Christians before we were party men; we had to meet on the very things that divided us, not to be raised immediately above our divisions but to acknowledge that we had all alike need of God's grace and that we were all dependent upon one another in the learning of His truth.

It was in the sphere of politics, where it was most difficult of all, that we had to learn humility—in the political arena where it was normal to have to appear blameless and to identify the wrongs of society with the people to whom we were opposed, where we were always under the temptation to burn with indignation against the folly and wickedness of other people. Just here, where the acknowledgment of error and limitation seemed a confession of weakness, we had to learn to stand like that before God and be willing to be seen standing like that before our community. That was the cross; and it was nowhere more difficult to take up than here. It was a cross that could not be taken up alone; it had to be taken up, with the strengthening of God's grace, by men who were standing together.

For Adam Baillie it would be one kind of cross, laying himself bare, perhaps, to new thoughts which he had never allowed himself to harbour, taking away battlements from his life which he had always considered to be essential; perhaps, hardest of all, having to be seen changing his mind under the influence of people for whom he had no regard.

For John Forsyth it might be the cross of learning that it is easier to burn with indignation against that man on the other side, that class, that employers' federation, than to let the fire of God's righteousness do its cleansing with ourselves, to escape the judgment of it by looking outside ourselves for the evil, and to take no blame before God. It was the old superstition of the Beltane fire, to believe we could get rid of evil by the magic of identifying it with something that could be burned up and destroyed, something outside ourselves, a system, a group of people. Fixing the blame there we could set ourselves to eliminate it there, blind to what there was of it in ourselves.

For me it was at once the denying of the easier friendship with these two men for the sake of a friendship which demanded what I was not always willing to give, the cost of speaking the truth.

This was to be the way of men's saving; and we had been losing the way. Where did we have the fellowship in which men learned what was sore to learn, in humility before God and before one another? Where was the readiness to go out ahead of other men at the points where sin was most deeply entrenched in human life, where it did not seem possible to obey God and all the weight of argument was for making the

best of things as they were, where the world divided us and
He seemed to be asking the impossible? We had to be like an
army, advancing into enemy territory. The army must have
its companies; it must be based on the small unit; it must
bring men together where they can be taught.

The Kingdom is already here where these two or three are
gathered. As they stumble their way to a word of difficult
forgiveness Christ is with them. As they make themselves
willing to learn what He has to teach them they become more
humble towards one another.

This was what should have been there for Jacob and Mary
Telfer; and it had not been there. If they had been in a
company of people who were learning to break through these
barriers they might have been saved from the building up of
their own barriers and from the dumbness of evil that came
upon them within their own home.

Kenneth Sanderson and his father needed it. They were
hardening towards each other, till the day when sudden anger
might come upon them like destruction. They ought to be
where Christ's people were learning to withstand that evil.
If they had been praying together for other people they might
have learned better how to pray for each other. If they had
been denying themselves the easy judgment against their
neighbours they might have been on the way to being delivered
from it between themselves.

Will Mortimer and his ploughman needed it, the " boss "
and the " hand," the master as the payer of wages and the
exacter of work, the servant as the human machine for the
labour of the farm, meeting each day across their duties and
each day seeing each other less and less as a brother for whom
Christ died. Yet on the Sacrament day they were on the same
church path and sitting in the same pew, saying, like Adam

Baillie and Forsyth, " Forgive us " and " We believe," and
handing to each other the cup of common guilt and common
pardon. But the Sacrament was never known to them in the
place where it was to be potent for them. It had no meaning
where they lived and worked.

Somehow the real things of the world, the actual divisions,
the dilemmas, had to be brought where they could be yielded
to God. And they must be brought in the men divided and in
dilemma. And men must be taught to bring them, not only
in the services of the Lord's Day, which are the summing up
of worship, but where worship is of the " two or three
gathered together." There, with their neighbours, gathered
perhaps in a farm kitchen, they could learn what confession is,
and forgiveness, and the intercession for a brother's need, and
the thankfulness for God's mercies. They could find new
urgency in the Word and new meaning in the Sacrament.

Master and servant; younger generation and older; wife
and husband; citizens and their rulers—where had I seen them
brought together under a single word? It was a word I had
heard more often than any other in Crainie when men re-
counted to me how they had " had words " with each other:
" I couldn't submit to it." But in the Word of God we are
told what seems like the opposite. We are to learn to submit.
And for realism it is set out in the relationships where submission seemed hardest: " Servants, submit yourselves to your
masters"; " Wives, submit yourselves to your husbands ";
" Submit yourselves to them that have the rule over you " ...
everywhere that men found it most intolerable to submit.

These were the points in the first days of the Faith where
the Christian in his new-found liberty would be tempted to
break out of the difficult relationship and to seek where he
could live more closely to the Gospel with those who shared

his faith; the wife, bound perhaps to a husband who did not share her faith; the servant, conscious of his new dignity as one declared the son of God, working in a system which gave the master the power of life and death over his slaves; the new democracy of believers, eager to throw off every yoke, and living under Roman imperialism and its army of occupation. And the Word came to them to stay where they were, to give themselves to the difficult relationship because it was there that God's light would break forth for them.

Submission was no giving in; it was a determination not to give up the fight because the odds were too heavily against them, to remain in contact with the men whom they might have every human reason to get away from, the rulers who showed no understanding and might even be threatening them with persecution. They were not to contract out of the community and leave " the powers that be " to go their way, unrebuked by the life that Christ had brought for men; they were to submit themselves to them, to remain under them, and to bear their witness for Christ there.

A supreme temptation in the first days of the Church was for believing men to go on the defensive, to withdraw into their own community of the Faith, to let the evil world go by, to be more intent on being saved than on saving. And they were put on their guard by this word. Christ had submitted Himself to sinful men. And out of His submission had come the miracle of the Resurrection.

This word had been spoken for men in these first days; but now in Crainie, when I looked for the points of sharpest temptation, I saw them just where they had been then; in the relationship of master and servant, husband and wife, younger and older, in the tension of politics—in Will Mortimer and his ploughman; in the Telfers; in Kenneth Sanderson and his father; in Adam Baillie and John Forsyth. At each point one of them could say " This is unjust—this is more than I can endure." And just at these points they had to endure the Word of God, commanding them to stay where they were, to submit themselves to the relationship which cried out to them to quit, and just there to learn to take up their cross daily.

And the Word came to us that there was to be no bearing of this cross alone: " Ye are members one of another." We were to be one body, fitting together as members of one body, knowing one another at the level of tensions and defeats, and Christ's victories. We could not hear the Word truly unless we were together to speak of the things which God was making plain to us, unless we were able to say like Ananias— " Brother Saul, the Lord who appeared unto thee hath sent me." Neither Saul nor Ananias was able alone to understand what had been revealed. Unless we had part with one another we could not have part with Him.

That was why we were bidden to eat of the one bread of the Sacrament and divide it among ourselves, as if we were saying " This that is given for me is given also for your need." For the making of the miracle we had to offer the bread of our division to Him, the bread which had come from the work of Mortimer and his ploughman in the heat of their antagonism, and, receiving it again, divide it among ourselves as the bread of His sacrifice for all of us alike. The bread of the community's struggle for its livelihood, the occasion of its disputes, is given back as the communion of Christ's heavenly kingdom. The Church is created at the very point where men have broken with one another, out of the very stuff of their divisions, out of the breakdown of their community.

How could Mortimer and his ploughman see this in the bread if they did not know that their enmity over the winning of the bread crucified Christ afresh? How could Crainie feel the urgent life that was in the Cup, this same Cup that had ministered the Sacrament to their fathers for more than three hundred years and had gone to the hills with them in the days when Anthony Murray was driven from his kirk, if Crainie did not know that it drew the blood of Christ's sacrifice?

14

How WERE we to come to the understanding of it? Perhaps it had been easier for men in the old days. Their work held them more closely together; they knew evil, not only in what it did to a man's character but in the effect it had upon what his hands produced and what he made of his dealings with other men; they knew good in what they actually saw of a man's worth in his trade or his craft. Was it not easier for them to discern where their true good lay?

Not so long since in Crainie the children had watched the mill-wheel turning to give them their meal; the cobbler bent at his last, making their boots; the women at their weaving; the little shops with the quarter-pane windows, supplying all that could not be produced in Crainie itself—almost every house telling of a trade which Crainie could not do without; and nearly every man a Crainie man by birth, carrying on where his father, or someone else's father, left off.

They could listen to the ploughman complaining about the shoes of his horse and hear the smith's "Man, I'm fair ashamed." They could see the tailor at work on the plaids, sending his cloth out to be tested by the same shepherds who had clipped and carded it. They could watch the joiner estimating the value of timber, judging whether it had been rightly thinned and felled at a proper maturity.

They had grown up amongst men and women all depending

on each other's work. The broken word was a word broken between men they knew; the dependable word was part of the character of the man whose work they saw every day.

Something had gone out of our dealings with one another as the mill and the smithy, the tailor and the little shops, had been taken from us.

But what was it? And why had it gone? Was it just, as people said, changed days?

Crainie's ways had changed, as every country community had changed. We were not the self-enclosed parish any longer; and we belonged to a new generation which was everywhere bewildered by what had come upon the earth and might still be to come. But that was not the whole answer. How was it that, out of that generation, living in such close relationship, so " God-fearing " and mindful of the things that endure, another generation had come which did not hold in the same way to the faith of their fathers? Was it because of the new pressure of the world's doubts and uncertainties? Or could it be that the older generation, for all its steadfastness, had known less than it thought about the issues of life and had sent out its children unready for what was to come? Did the very closeness of its community, and the seeming security, encourage men to forget that the human heart is desperately wicked? Did the kindliness of the community sometimes conceal from its folk that they had to reach out beyond kindliness?

Was it just changed days? Or was it that we had come unprepared into the changed days, unprepared for the break up of the old, unready to make exploration into the new?

Perhaps the old community in Crainie had been too comfortable, in spite of its poverty of gear. Perhaps it had reckoned too much with the sins which disturbed its life and had left out of account the hidden sins, not looking into the darker depths.

The children coming after that generation had been faithful to religious observance; but their lives had been ruled by the keeping of the commandments rather than by the Gospel of a grace by which men are saved; and the next generation, growing up now, had little with which to face a cynical world.

They were paying the price, many of them, of inheriting a formal religion. Some were concerned only that the evils of the world should be held at bay while they had what they wanted out of life. Some had seen evils which must be fought and had crusaded against them; and many had been disillusioned when the victory did not bring what it had promised. Some had discovered, at the cost of despair and breakdown, that the evil they hated was in themselves. They had come unprepared into the fiery trial.

I could not wish Crainie back in those days. In the contentment and security men had often been made blind to what the Lord was requiring of them, and their children had grown up without a hunger and thirst for righteousness, though they may not have known what they lacked.

But how were we to find the hunger again? How were we to long for the very thing we had become more and more accustomed to do without? The answer for me was not in any book; but it came to me in a man.

Kenneth Sanderson had grown up at Wellwood as one of the indifferent. His father had kept his Sabbaths and " given of his substance " to the Kirk as the Lord had prospered him; but he had not given as the Lord had prospered him to the workmen in his factory. He kept the remembrance of God in His House, acknowledged the duty of moral uprightness, recognised that material prosperity had its obligations. All these commandments he had kept from his youth up; but he had never understood that uprightness does not save a man. He had learned in his youth the standard of conduct which was expected of him as a Christian; and, except for shortcomings and backslidings, he had tried to be faithful. It had laid the foundations of his business success and his home. He did not know that it had blinded him, made him at ease when he should have been disturbed.

Kenneth had grown up resentful of his father's assurance. He saw no connection between these Sabbath observances and what happened during his father's week. He became first of all critical and then rebellious. The sharp tension between good and evil which he could not find in his father's form of religion flared out before his eyes in what man was making of man in the day's work. Religion seemed to give its blessing to the fortunate ones and only a bare sympathy to those who were kept under. He believed passionately—but not in the way his father believed. He believed in what man had been meant to be; he rebelled against the despising, the classing of men as machine-hands, the housing of them in brick-row hovels, the breaking of mind and body in many of them, their casting away when the work had gone out of them.

He did not know what he believed about the Church's creeds; but he knew what he was for, and what he was against, there. He became a fighter in the cause of the " underdog." However confused the issues of good and evil sometimes were elsewhere—and he had seen them in confusion enough in his father—here they were clear; here was evil to be hit hard. We had lost community; and this was the proof of it.

Even in Crainie we had something to remind us of a life which had now disappeared. There was a croft not far from the manse where the walls of an old farm " toun " still stood:

five cottages which had housed a small community of weavers. They had grown their own flax, made their cloth, shared the labour of the fields and divided the reward. It had not been more than a bare livelihood; but it had bound men together instead of dividing them: it had given them the discipline of dependence and independence.

Some of the older folk in Crainie still remembered the families that had been brought up there.

The Lintwell had known no abundance; its families had lived often near the edge of privation. But there had been community; and something about it stirred the imagination as we stood in our disrupted society and wondered how men were to find community again.

But could the kind of community we were groping after be found by the wisdom of the new sciences—and higher living standards? Or were we on the edge of a mystery—were we involved in seeking the Kingdom even while we thought we were only seeking a better ordering of our industrial life?

The community, we were accustomed to say, is intended to hold men together in the necessities, to give them their livelihood, to keep them in the market for their labour, to enable them to share in what other men produce, to guarantee to them the basis of a decent life, to ensure them justice, to keep wrongdoers in check. But community of that kind did not satisfy the whole of man. And his dissatisfaction was the proof that even the secular community must look up to what man has it in him to be as well as down to the evils of insecurity from which he has to be protected.

Even the secular community, the community which is a compromise of conflicting interests, is always creating its own contradiction; the impulse to another kind of community which will have the power to draw out a different kind of capacity in men. The contradiction is the sign that it is men like ourselves, engaged together in the search for our basic needs, who are to inherit the Kingdom. It is to be a community made out of the stuff of human need. It is not to be a community of another kind in which we shall be delivered from necessity. It is to be born out of this very necessity we know.

When I stood looking at the old Lintwell cottages I was not sentimentalising. I was looking for a " toun " which had foundations as real as these and yet belonged to the new age which was coming upon us. I was not harking back to a lost community. I was taking the glimpses of what that community had been to remind me that man's work can be ordered not only to give him the physical necessities but to point him to the mystery of his own nature, to what he has to learn standing by his neighbour.

The Lintwell had been a small unit; it had done, on that scale, what it had been intended to do; it had given men an insight into the community to come, even while it was binding them together in the community of their labouring. The ruins were a symbol of what our generation had to discover again in our more complex communities.

What was needed had to be found by ordinary men doing ordinary work—men prone to seek their own good at the expense of their neighbour and often having no use for him, yet also with something in them which impelled them to lay down their lives for others.

After they had organised themselves and achieved juster rewards, after they had benefited by new inventions, there was always something still lacking. Here, at the Lintwell, where half a dozen men washed together at the common spiggot on Sunday mornings before church, there had been a clue. Along at the village, with its common byre and grazing, there had been another. But the Church itself had lost it in the very day when the world needed it most desperately, because the Church had become conformed to a world which had lost it. " Industry is depersonalised," said the Church's pronouncements; " the man is lost in the machine." But the Church itself was depersonalised; the Church itself had become an organisation in which man did not meet with man as the Gospel had intended them to meet. How then was the Church to be a light to the world?

God has made His dwelling with men for their saving, where they dwell, where they work, where they grope for a life which their work seems to deny them. This is the Gospel. But the Church was no longer the Church where they dwelt; it was an occasional gathering of men, withdrawn from where they dwelt. How then could the Church be doing God's saving work?

One of the Church's temptations is to think of itself as standing over against the world, countering the world's unbelief with its own belief. But it is not as clear-cut as that. When we think like that we are revealing our lack of understanding of the mission Christ has laid upon us. We are evading involvement in the world; we are sheltering in an imaginary purity; we are blind to the nature of the presence of God in the world, and to the presence of the Tempter in the Church.

The whole world is full of the living God. In their unbelief as well as in their belief men bear witness to Him. Believers or unbelievers, the shape of their lives is determined by what they are towards God. When they become inflamed by self-interest it is more than an outburst of evil from within them; they are turning in fear from the presence of the Spirit of God, who is putting it into their hearts "not to seek their own." The form of their fear determines the form of their denial. If God were not with them, and if He were not like that, they would not be like this in their evil. The sinfulness of men is not an erratic eruption from some flaw in human nature; it is a disobedience which takes its shape from what it disobeys.

When men become obsessed with pride it is more than an aggressive assertion of themselves over their brothers; it is a determination not to be involved in the humility of Christ which is burning in their hearts so that they cannot but know it.

All our sin is sin against God, sin created in the presence of God, sin called up in us by our refusal of what God is. Our worldliness takes its shape from that other kind of worldliness in which God condescends to make Himself one with sinful men.

Unless the Church knows the full pressure of the unbelief in men by dwelling with them in it, it cannot be where God is; it is creating an unreal refuge of its own as shelter from God and what He is doing in the world; and it cannot be the instrument of God's help. He is not only in the Church, with the people of God, urging them to go out with Him into the world; He is in the world, ruling and over-ruling, despised and rejected, yet working out His purposes through His rejection, calling the Church to be with Him in the world, to learn of Him in the world, to stand with unbelieving men in the world and be given His help in common with them.

And there is more than that. Unbelieving men bear the marks of the God who girds them even when they do not know Him; and believing men have to learn something of what they do not yet know of God from unbelievers—another hard discipline.

The fanatical reformer of human society, who will use any means to achieve his ends, believes in some community of men because the Spirit of the Lord has touched him—while many believing men may not yet have the desire to seek for it. He sins, too, against his brother men for the achieving of it because the Spirit of the Lord has touched him, and he has rejected the way that the Spirit would have him go. But who is to judge between the unbelief of the believer and the belief of the unbeliever but God alone? It is all entangled together. His saving help must be given to all together.

Christ had to empty Himself, and make Himself of no reputation, and become obedient to death amongst criminals. Under His Cross, although we have a sharper perception of right and wrong, we are not good people set over against bad. We are all sinful men; some of us with belief stained by unbelief. We are one body—one body with all sinful men, as Christ's Body is given for all sinful men. We are in full community there, and only there.

This is the paradox which is at the heart of the Church's existence: that only a Church which is so involved in the world that it cries out in despair because of its involvement, and is even shaken in its own faith, can be the means of saving the world. It may be assured in faith, believe in the promises, have the confidence of a people upon whom God has set His heart—yet it lives every day on the edge of the unbelievable; that He can humble Himself so far, that He can have hope for the worst.

Kenneth had believed, like most of us, that we could leave the community of the day's work to the politicians, the economists, the industrialists; fight out the battles there, form the new plans there; and leave the community of man's spiritual being to the Church. But it is in the community of the day's work that men believe and disbelieve, obey the Spirit and resist the Spirit, give shape to the Kingdom or to the demonic powers of darkness.

Kenneth spoke about the depersonalisation which had come with the large groupings of industry, as if it were a matter for technical adjustment; but it was not the mere size of the industrial units or the nature of their work which took away human relationships from men. Crainie had lost it too, though men still worked here in twos and threes. This was not an evil created by the new age; it was an evil which industrialism had magnified into vast proportions and built into the structure of man's common life; but it was fundamentally the sin of evading what God intended man to mean to man.

It was there between Kenneth and his father, in their home, just as surely as between the workers in the factory. They did not see eye to eye; so they went their own ways. They achieved tolerance, for their own comfort—but their very tolerance was an acknowledgment that they were not going to try to reach anything better; they had given up; they had achieved a balance through non-interference. They had levelled down their relationship; they had lost all that, as father and son, they should have meant to one another, all that they were meant to be taught of God together.

It was the evasion, by mutual consent, of the consequences of evil—not its overcoming. And it had the additional evil of blinding them to the evil which was there, making them complacent about it, deluding them into thinking that this was the kind of peace between them which God wanted, when it was the root of all disobedience.

"We need pilot schemes of community," Kenneth said; and stood looking at the ruins of the Lintwell cottages. But there was the ruin of a home at Wellwood; and a pilot scheme needed there.

The recovery of what God intended for these two men, living together, would not immediately solve the problems of their factory; but two new men could go into the factory, knowing what the Lord required of them, learning what to look for between man and man, and what to regard as sin.

We had lost community; but we had lost it in the home and in the Church as well as in our industrial society—and we had lost it because we had been content with less than God willed for us. We had allowed ourselves to rest, like Kenneth and his father, in the community of compromise and adjustment, in a balance of conflicting interests, when God was saying to us that here we could not find the life for which He had created us. In this breakdown of our society and our homes, and in the futility of the conventional Church, we were under His judgment; and we were proving the destiny purposed for us which our deeds were strenuously denying.

But how was Kenneth to submit himself to his father? It was not by agreeing with all that his father said, nor by becoming compliant. It was by daring to let his father see him as he was—instead of as he wanted to appear in his father's eyes. It was by being willing to expose himself to the kind of love which he and his father had never known, with its cost to himself, and without the foregone certainty that his father would meet him half-way. It was by giving up the language and the manner of tolerance and allowing himself to speak as a man who thought it possible that he might be mistaken.

Kenneth and his father were constantly submitting reports to one another. But they did not submit themselves, sinful man to sinful man, under God's grace, to find together what each by himself could never find. They were realistic about things, and unrealistic as people.

If the home which was to be the type and example for the Church was itself a place of evasion and compromise, if the Church which was to be a saving community was itself not a community, how were we to be the light of a world which was groping for these very things and yet giving itself over to the powers which destroy them? If the salt itself had lost its savour wherewith was it to be salted?

" We need pilot schemes," Kenneth said. But most of all we needed pilot schemes in people.

15

IT WAS typical of our day that in the cobbler's back shop men were bent over their arguments (was there a God?—could there be a God when evil had its way unchecked?—could there be a God of mercy when millions died in suffering?) while less than a mile away there were happenings which they would have found it hard to explain without God.

If the men at the cobbler's were to look for God in Crainie they would have to choose whether to look first at what seemed to deny Him and argue how there could be a God at all, or to look where life was changed and took on the marks of Christ, and ask how it came about.

That mystery was in life, however we argued. There was a mystery of evil; but there was a mystery, too, in godliness.

With his doubts wearing his mind into ruts, Kenneth found something happening to him which no doubts could reach. But when he came to me it was to cry with Paul " Who will deliver me? "

" I've been trained to be sure of myself. It's my business to be sure—and to let people see that I'm sure. Now I've to throw all that kind of confidence out at the window—and let people see that I've thrown it out. I've to be ready to admit I'm the kind of man who can get things wrong, who has to be checked up every day to bring him back to the right. But how can I when I've been built up the opposite way ever since I was at school? Every day in the office adds to it; and every time I listen to the politicians; and every time I read the newspapers. And then the Gospel says, Repent and be changed. But how can I want to be changed? How can I repent of what I'm trying every day to be?"

It was no new dilemma; it was only the shape of it, and the sharpness of it, that was new.

No one has ever been able to want it enough; no one has ever been able to repent enough. We have become men who do not have it in them to want it. That is why we need a Saviour.

I had to say the old word: "It isn't your repentance that's going to get you through—it's Christ's repentance for you, Christ repenting for you before you are able to repent for yourself, paying the price before you are willing to give anything. You've got to humble yourself to take it."

That was where he had to be, even if he did not know what words he was to say, and was there with nothing but his need and the assurance that in his need he was where he ought to be.

This is the kind of prayer which comes hardly when we are trained to put the best face on everything. In the day of adversity, at the end of our resources, with no wisdom of our own about the way ahead, we often recover what it means to go into God's presence, as Kenneth might go into Crainie Kirk and make himself stand before the Table, believing only that he was placing himself where hope was to be found, standing there blindly, waiting for what seemed to belong to that place, although not knowing what to ask. But when we are conscious of our powers, confident of our wisdom, it does not come easily to humble ourselves.

To go in this kind of prayer before God is not uplifting or

reassuring or even comforting; it is only taking ourselves where we belong; thankful to be able to stand there; awaiting anything that He may show, whether it is reassuring or disturbing, a light for the way before us or an understanding that we are not yet to be shown where we are to go.

This is not a new or a strange position for men to be in; it is the position they are always in; but they do not know it because their eyes are blinded by the world, and they will not ask and will not accept.

When we stand like this, whether by compelling circumstance in God's providence or by our own feeling after the truth, we begin to forget ourselves, deny ourselves, lose ourselves, the selves which are keeping us from God—not by seeking to be saved but by putting ourselves where God can do what He wills with us; not by saying the right words to Him but by letting Him say His word to us.

It is the beginning of the life which seems always to be beyond us, to be beyond even our desiring because we have come to desire other things more.

This is where we stop having our own ambitions for ourselves. We do not know what is good for us, so how can we seek what we do not know? This is where we stop putting ourselves in the centre, asserting ourselves and defending ourselves—because it does not seem important any more. It is here that these things must be broken in us, and we must be willing to let them go, before we can hope to live the new life amongst men: turning the other cheek to the smiter, going a second mile with him who asks us to go one, loving our enemies. That life has to be lived with God, found where we meet with God, before it can be lived where we meet with men, though it is indeed one life, and in a flash of a single moment we are before God as well as before our brother, as

I had been when I stood looking at John Forsyth's window; but we must know God's humility towards us before we can be humble in the presence of arrogant men. As the scholars would say, the Christian life cannot be an ethic until it has been a worship. There is no fellowship, no community, no Church, without this.

I did not see Kenneth again for some weeks. When he came next there was something new in him.

" I'm beginning to understand," he said, " what Paul meant. It's what Christ has done—not what I've been trying to do. It makes you tremble for yourself; and it makes you confident. It makes you want to fall down on your face before Him; and it sets you on your toes. Why doesn't the Church seem like that ? "

He told me how he had once seen an old, crippled peasant in France hobbling along the dusty road to Mass, as if his whole life depended upon it. " We'd say it was fear and superstition. But is it better to be a Protestant, and free from all superstition, and lie on your back on the hillside when the church bell is calling you? I watched these people touching holy water to remind themselves that they had to be saved. Is it better to be a Protestant and come and go easy-minded, and think you've no need of saving? There's been nothing to make me realise that we're all caught in a net and can't get out of it. You've never made me shudder to be the kind of person I am. The confessional has been turned out—that's maybe putting the priest between us and God—but you haven't put anything else in its place to shake us and make us understand that we're in the toils of sin, and sin is death. You preach the love of God—but not the love of God which makes us tremble for ourselves and fall down."

It was true. I had trembled more to stand before men and

their judgment in my preaching than to stand before the holiness of God and be the preacher of His judgment.

I had been left, by the tradition of my Church, to decide what I should preach, to seek alone how I should be a voice for other men's prayers. Week by week I had to make myself the arbiter of what would be read from God's Word, what would be asked for in prayer, what would be confessed, what would be remembered in thanksgiving, and in what words of psalm and hymn these people present before God would speak to Him. It was my service, in my words, in my choosing of other men's words.

But I had missed the meaning of the tradition. I had not understood why the freedom and responsibility were there. What had come down to us was not a casualness in the form of our worship. It was high doctrine of the Church.

If we are to speak for Christ, it said, we must acknowledge Him and what He has done for us. We must be willing, like Paul, to be a spectacle, a gazing-stock, an open witness to the power of the Cross, to the need for the Cross, so that men can have no doubt why we stand there.

That had not been in my ministry until I knew for myself what makes a man fall down on his knees and cry " My Lord and my God "; and I could not call my people with the tone of voice of such a man to worship and fall down.

The tradition in our Church was that the minister of Christ should be in himself the urgency of the Gospel and the means of the people's offering of worship. It was not the unwisdom of men but the deepest mystery of our calling. The minister was to be no mere offerer of a sacrifice for his people. He was himself to be a sacrifice, himself an offering, a faith for them before God, so that their faith might be kindled. The need of the Cross, his need of the Cross, must be visible before them.

He must be known as a man who, in his daily ministry, acknowledges his need of forgiveness and rebuke. This was one part of what it meant for him to submit himself to them.

There can be no boasting if that is what we are and why we are there, no display of our gifts, no eloquence as men usually think of eloquence, no question of having done well. We have been there as a testimony. Because we have come to know ourselves as sinful men we are prepared to go up into a pulpit and lead other sinful men along with ourselves into the presence of God, casting ourselves upon His mercy, thankful for His grace. We are "as a brand plucked from the fire."

To be known for that is to let our confidence, our assurance and our gifts, be broken every day and laid on the altar. This is the sacrifice which enables us to minister, to go into the holy of holies, taking our people with us—in our humble words, as well as in the great words of the Church. It is for this that we are given freedom, freedom from enslavement to a liturgy, freedom from rigid adherence to forms.

I had sometimes had it in my heart to wish that in Crainie Kirk we could be bidden to fall upon our knees while our sin was being confessed and to rise to our feet to hear the Gospel of our redemption read. But perhaps even in that I had been looking everywhere for the power to move men but in myself —the appointed instrument of God—evading the demand that I should myself be the sacrifice, myself the confession of faith uttered before men.

I could not—because I had not come to that confession myself with all that was in me. And it was this boy who sent me to my knees now because my eyes had been opened. I had spoken a word to bring him to Christ—and the word had come back to me to bring me closer myself than I had ever been to my Saviour and Lord.

How could men be brought to re-birth except by the urgency of God's word breaking in upon them? And was it likely that the urgency of His word would reach them through the tones of a man who did not know the urgency in himself? God has many ways of reaching a man's soul, and He can work through poor and unworthy words; but the preaching of a man who is easy-minded about himself clouds the vision of his hearers so that they cannot see God.

If there is no urgency in the preaching there is no urgency in the fellowship, no need to be gathered together as men in desperation to receive the promised salvation, no need to support and strengthen one another in fervent prayer, no urgency to go out to seek and to save.

The next time we met I had something more to say to him—but so had he to me.

" I think that there has been something in the Church itself that has been making it more difficult for me to repent. I've been brought up in a Christian home. I've attended Church since I was five. I went to Sunday School till I was fourteen, and a Bible Class for three years after that. I came through the graded scheme which prevents anybody like me slipping from the Church. I'm the person you stand up and tell about in your statistics. I've had all the right teaching and I've been kept safely within the Church . . . And here I've been, until now, thinking I had no need of repentance—knowing all the Gospel story but never being halted at a crucial word, never brought to the point, always reassured when I should have been shaken, always turned away from the terrible dilemma that we see what we ought to be and can't reach it, that we haven't got it in us to repent and yet if we don't repent we have no place in the Kingdom. You asked me to your catechumens'

class. You taught me all that I ought to believe. I had been
baptised into the Church. I had been kept within the Church.
I was making up my mind to remain within it. Everything
was in order, but I believe it all hid from me the very thing
you've had to say to me now. It prevented me seeing myself
as I was. It flattered me that I was good enough to face God
when I wasn't even facing myself. And all the time that Bible
was lying open in the pulpit, saying the truth about me; and
you were too polite to let it speak. But you've let it speak now.

" I don't think I'm just excusing myself—I should have
known. I'm thinking of what's to come next. The people
I work with don't believe in this. The set-up of my job
doesn't allow for this. We have our ways of working. We
have our orders. It's the business that rules—we have to fit into
it. How do I live a new life there? If the Church is real that's
where we have to be the Church—not just in the evenings
when we meet with our friends in the church buildings. How
am I to witness these? How am I to help them to see this
Gospel and not this confusing Church? "

He was asking me the question which within a few years
was to send the Church to its knees. I had no answer. The
whole Church was soon to discover it had no answer, if by
answer we mean a solution to the dilemma which will enable
a man to become easy-minded.

How are Christian men, when they are a few, to shape the
decisions of industry, to mould the policies of commerce;
and, if they cannot, how far are they to go in accepting the
decisions of others and allowing them to become determinative
in their lives? If they rebel, are they to contract out of society
and earn their bread in a community of their own?

These were soon to be no academic questions but a searching
of what the community of Christ's people is to do about the

wider community in which it is set. The age of the atom was soon to be upon us; and men were to be given powers they had never been given before—power to create new wealth and new control over nature and to be inflamed with new desires and the capacity for swift attainment of them. The greatest change in human life since the discovery of fire and the harvesting of the first crops was near. The limitations which had been an involuntary discipline were to be suddenly swept away; and men were to be left in new nakedness before God, asking what was the end of it all, what was the ultimate meaning of things which would give a man his bearings in all this new bewilderment. And over all was to hang the threat of the hydrogen bomb, symbol of the answer which could be death to mankind—and men unready for the choice thrust upon them, standing without the guiding light their fathers had known.

It was the old dilemma raised to unimagined dimensions: how were we called to be Christians in the heart of this moral turmoil, where, in despair of a purpose, men were giving all their energies to the perfecting of the machine which increased their confusion, to the mounting of greater production, giving themselves over to their own creation, worshipping the work of their hands? Many would come, like Kenneth, and say " Who will deliver us? " And the Church would discover it had no solution for their perplexity and despair. The only answer was to stand before God without an answer and, in the midst of the ultimate agony of human life, ask what He would have them to do, and, in asking it without any confidence of their own, find themselves one with the whole bewildered body of mankind under its own sentence of death.

Kenneth was one of the portents of what was to come. He was seeing what many of us within the Church were as yet unable to recognise: that, by this despair coming upon men, the Church would be re-born, that by the loneliness of those who stood where they could not feel they had power to achieve anything, the Church would discover again that this is how it is always meant to be. It is not any strange trial that is come upon us but the universal lot of sinful men, facing death and damnation—felt newly now because the old supports of an accepted morality are taken away and the traditional comforts of community are no longer with us on the factory floor and at the scientist's bench.

The dilemma was not new; but the sharpness of it was to be such as men had seldom known; and Christian men, in the midst of it, were to compel the Church to see it as it certainly had not been seen before in our day.

What were they to do when man's world was breaking under him? How could they stand fast? No answer from the inner comfort of the Christian fellowship could suffice. They had to stand in the places of the world's work where there was no such fellowship. They had to learn that, standing there as Christ's few, they were not in fact separated off from those who did not believe, but brought closer to them. This was the paradox, that, knowing ourselves Christ's, we still had to stand with those who did not acknowledge Him, knowing ourselves no better than they, with no greater wisdom of our own, perhaps with less spirit than they with which to seek the Kingdom. We still had to learn from the children of this world, even while we stood witnesses for Christ amongst them.

We were in the same desperate situation as they—some of them conscious of it, some totally indifferent; and we could not be delivered except by seeking deliverance along with them. We only increased the confusion when we set before them a Church which was supposed to have an easy answer to all their perplexity.

The despair itself is not anything strange to the man who has come to know what he is and how he stands with God—how he can do nothing, faced by these ultimate dilemmas; how he has no solution, no way out of the breakdown of his society. But when men have not stood there before God their despair may make them, instead, angry and embittered about the ills of mankind, exasperated with their neighbour, resigned to meeting violence with violence in the disputes of the nations.

This is the fiery trial through which we must come. This is our destiny, to be purified " yet so as by fire." This is where we ought to be because of what we are, what we have made of ourselves and our communities. Despair is right for us, if it is the right despair, despair before God, acknowledgment before Him that we do not have it in us now to do what we know is commanded. It is the truth about our condition, the condition of our communities and nations, of humanity: and, when it is the despair of men who know that what has come upon them is God's judgment on what they are, their cry of " Who will deliver us ? " is already a cry of faith.

And the God who delivers nations is the same God. He has the same purpose. His ways are the same. The confusion of the nations has the same meaning as the despair of a man. But there is something in the very nature of the nation which hides this from us. We have to be governed by having our competing interests subordinated to the common good. That is the necessary compromise of our common life. But it conditions us to the acceptance of other compromises. It becomes a technique for living, a way of life, a basis for personal relationships—and, when it has reached as far as that, it has become a substitute for immediate obedience to what God is bidding us do. As a way of life it gives us a precarious kind of community, and a superficial contentment of mind as individuals; and it blinds us, when our society is threatened, to the reasons for its shaking. We are of a mind ready to see a failure of adjustment rather than a divine judgment.

Was it not this that was breaking in upon us when in our day men's hearts were failing them for fear of what was coming on the earth? But could it have any bearing on what we were to be as the Church of Christ in country places remote from the centres of tension—for us in Crainie?

We had this in common with those who were standing as Christ's few at the heart of the country's industry and commerce, that in our own way we had been called, some few of us, to see ourselves as a new kind of Church; not a confident institution working for human betterment but men and women unable to be to one another in close community what the Lord God desired us to be, failing to fulfil His commands because of human sinfulness, and driven to cry out as brethren in the same need. God was speaking to the same condition in us and saving us out of the same distresses, so that we began to forget our needs in rejoicing at the wonderful things He had done.

Before we parted, Kenneth asked me suddenly if he could make a new commitment of himself in the Communion Sacrament.

On the instant I could not find it in me to say that the Sacrament was four months away, and that our Church made no provision for his kind of need. The word in the New Testament about the other Sacrament flashed on me—" Can anyone forbid water that this man should not be baptised? " Could I forbid Christ's bread and cup to this man who desired them as an immediate pledge of his new life? It was not the

Church's bread; it was Christ's. I had to break the Church's practice for the sake of Christ's love.

As I bent towards him with Christ's cup next day I was more conscious than I had ever been that it was Christ and not I who ministered, He and not I who gave the promise that, as surely as the cup was taken to the lips, so sure was His grace. It had not been my ministry that had brought Kenneth here; it had been His; and He had brought us both together.

16

I HAD much more to learn after that of what it meant for a minister to submit himself to his people.

The young farm-workers would have said that they were on good terms with the minister. He sat with them in their bothies and organised their sports; but they had not spoken to him as they spoke to one another; they kept a special language for him and shut out most of the subjects which chiefly occupied their minds.

He talked to them in Bible Class about religion; but they did not talk religion to him. There was one-way traffic. It took a camp and a hill-trek before they felt they could say what might shock him.

I did not tell them, had been one ploughman's verdict. I told them all the things they ought to know about the Bible, what they ought to believe, the principles of Christian conduct; but I did not tell them how they were to check a fellow-worker without inciting him to resentment, how they were to "take a telling" from the farmer when they were in the wrong without answering back in anger, how to handle other men when they weren't acting straight, how long you should be patient and when you should speak out—and what all this had to do with God.

It was easy to answer that nobody could live another man's life for him; and I could not know the life of the farm-close from the inside; a minister could not be expert everywhere. But, as I made my rejoinder, I knew that I was not answering.

"You have been with me in my temptations," Christ had said. He had taken His men as far as that into His confidence, into the inmost places where even the Son of Man had to wrestle with doubt. He had not hidden from them when His soul was heavy and He did not know what to say, when the evil in man weighed on Him and He could only ask questions when He prayed. I had not taken these boys into my inmost places. I had not told them how they were to find these things for themselves.

I had taught them about prayer. But where had I learned myself the kind of prayer I could not hold back? It had been out on the edge of life, wrestling with confused impulses and finding myself thrown upon God's mercy; venturing out into the beginnings of compassion and meeting with misunderstanding; trying to forgive and receiving scorn, and, standing in the wreckage of what I had attempted to do, crying out to God that His purposes might not be frustrated because I had failed in them. I had not told them how that kind of prayer had come to me. I had been afraid and hidden this from them. And there could have been only one reason for keeping it back. I had not wanted them to see me as I was in these moments: entangled in my own uncertainties, shaken in my faith. I had preferred that they should keep the picture of me as a minister whom they could respect, not as a "brand plucked from the fire."

So they had learned from me that they ought to say their prayers. But they had been given no help to pray in the moment when the words of the farm-close broke in upon them and shattered their faith and their resolve—when, in their own way, they were as I had been, in temptation.

I had taught them that the Spirit of God " dwelleth in us "
—" closer is He than breathing, nearer than hands or feet."
But what did these words mean to them? What was it that
happened? What would be the signs of it in their working
day? And how did it come about?

I had assured them that it was true—but I had not told them
how I had found it to be true. Yet this had become the miracle
of miracles to me, the daily evidence of the love of God: that
He heard my cry in the midst of ordinary things and answered
me there. I had not told them; and it was not that I had
nothing to say.

" I come in the little things, saith the Lord "—I remembered
the verse—in things so small that we cannot believe they can
be His concern: the wrong done, so trivial that I have altogether forgotten it; the minor deception by which I evaded
the discomfort of acknowledging a fault; the momentary
boastfulness, scarcely worth thinking about now—but He
evidently thinks about it, or He would not reveal it to me and
show me how to make restitution.

What was happening at these moments was no throw-up
from my subconscious mind. I could not believe that. It
was often a bidding to do what had never entered my
mind.

When I cried out for the help which someone needed and
it was not in me to give, something was given, often, which
was not mine. I knew because it was an answer for the need
beyond the need as I saw it; an answer with all the marks of
Christ in it.

I would be frustrated in the doing of something which I
knew was right for me to do, unable to see how it was
to be done, and suddenly it would be made plain to me that

I was trying to do it in my own way and not His; and in the moment of realising it I would become willing to give up my way and be ready to wait for His.

I would be perplexed whether to continue in a work and I would find myself enabled to write or speak some word which I knew beyond all questioning to be from Him; and my way, at least the next step of it, would again become clear. He would bring to mind the visit I had forgotten to make, the letter not written, the name gone from my memory and needed now for His purposes.

He would help me to understand the meaning of the sullenness of a little girl, disappointed because her impulse of helpfulness in the preparing of some meal had gone wrong, and uncover an unfairness in my anger with her; and I said, He must have been with us there in the kitchen, taking to do with the preparation of the meal and the washing-up of its dishes.

He comes in the little things, to break the hardness of our hearts. These are the moments of knowing. And if He gives Himself like that to us, what have we to fear? This was what I had been slowly learning.

But to tell these boys this I had to tell them, with chapter and verse from the book of my life, how it had been with me while I did not know these things and while I was learning them—how I had wanted the help but not the Helper, the guiding but not the Guide, not His Spirit, not His holiness, not His humility, not the kind of life which goes His way and loves with His love.

I had taught them how the Bible was God's Word to men, how it had been given to us for our instruction, how it set before us God's saving work in Jesus Christ. But I had never told them how, when I had been set on a course which would have led to the destruction of all that God was intending for me and to the wrecking of another life, words leapt to my mind which brought me to a sudden halt, like Saul on the Damascus road, and overpowered me with a realisation of what I was about to do. They were Bible words, grown familiar to me from my reading when I had no thought but to fulfil a duty, now become urgent words from the heart of God Himself. I had laid up for that moment the means for Him to speak to me, the only words which could have any power to alter me in the heat of that moment on the edge where decision is taken by a flash of impulse and cannot be undone in years of regret.

This was the Bible as they should have known it—the book to keep teaching us the mighty acts of God and "the way wherein we should walk," but the book, too, which at any moment might become, at the touch of the Spirit of God, the word for the farm bothy and the farm-close. And I had not told them. I had held it back from them. They were not with me in my temptations, nor I with them in theirs. All this was what I must now tell them.

Had it not been a sign of something lacking in my trust in God too? I had trusted myself where I was uncertain, but I had held back where I was confident that I knew my way. I had yielded myself to His correction when I had known myself to be in the wrong—but what of the wrong in me of which I was not aware? I was a sinful man down to the depths, deeper than I could ever know myself; and it was the depths of me He must have, the whole of me, all that lay beyond my understanding as well as all that came up into it.

Sometimes I had a glimpse into the depths. I would hear that a dying man wanted to see me; and across my mind would come a flicker of thankfulness—or was it pride?—that

I was able to be the kind of minister he would send for in his last hours; then, as swift, a horror that such a thought could enter my mind; and, as quickly as the horror, another thankfulness that I was able to feel horror and see my pride for what it was . . . always deeper and deeper, further into the inmost recesses of my self, this love of self, beyond my understanding, beyond my power to repent, an unplumbed depth of sin.

That was why Christ had to give all of Himself for me, the very depths of His life which even He could not plumb, for the sinfulness I cannot plumb.

That was what it meant, that nothing in us, nothing at all, can separate us from His love.

I remembered how Dr. Christopher had gone south to London from here many years ago to seek for the son who had dishonoured his home and left father and mother in silence about what had become of him. There was no address to guide him. Only after many days was the name of the street discovered; and when the old minister, with his white hair, stood at the end of it he knew it was beyond him to go from door to door of its length. But a street musician came by just then and Dr. Christopher stopped him. Did he know an old air—one that had been a favourite in the manse when the children were young? Would he walk with him along the street as he played? And he told him why.

So they went slowly, the street musician and the old minister with his hat in his hand so that his face could be seen, taking this last slender chance to find where his son was who had no use for him, seeking him who had no understanding of the love in his father's heart.

He did not succeed that day; but he left with us who came after in Crainie and Burnfoot a memory which made us ask where he had learned that love which cannot be separated by anything at all from the one loved.

I had thought often of the humility of Jesus; but I had never thought of the humility of the Holy Spirit. Not an influence only, giving us thoughts of holiness—this was something greater and more terrible. It was the unbelievable thing which made Peter cry out when Christ knelt down before him to wash the dirt of the road from his feet—something to recoil from, even while we were filled with wonder at it; a love we wished to hold at bay, to keep back until we had made ourselves more worthy of it. That He is with us when we believe —this is easy to understand. That He is with us in our unbelief, that He helps our unbelief—this is what our minds find it hard to comprehend. . . . God so strangely the humblest in Crainie.

I still could not believe with my mind all that it meant; but I became able now to see a little further. That He was still with me—this was the simple miracle which included all other miracles.

For Him to be with me after all that I had been and all that I had left undone—this was mercy unmerited; and every day I was living under it. This was the Kingdom here with me now—the promise of the best robe.

It might seem to me when I did evil that He was hidden and remote; but it was His patience I was seeing, the terribleness of His love, that He keeps me in life while I abuse life, that He continues His gifts to me while I turn them to my destruction, that He allows me so far to go my own way till I am willing to go His—His silence the evidence of His presence.

This is His judgment, that we are allowed to live without Him in His very presence; that we have to be allowed to live under the shadow of this world's death while the true light is shining. While we are imagining that there is no punishment for those who violate the Kingdom, misreading His patience and misunderstanding His humility, we are under the punishment. We have made it for ourselves before His face. We are separated from Him, whose love will not allow Him to be separated from us.

I had still been separating myself, for all that I believed, holding myself back from God and man. Even when I had gone to John Purdie in prison I had held back something I should have given. When Purdie was in prison Christ was in prison; He was bearing the wrongdoing. To come to Purdie in prison was to come to Him. To give myself to Purdie, holding nothing back, was to give myself to Christ. But I had held something back. I had not opened my heart. I had not said what I would have said if I had been giving all of myself. When Purdie was a stranger amongst his own people in Crainie, Christ was a stranger; when we took Purdie in we took Him in. But if I had been giving all of myself to Him I should have given Purdie something that I knew I had not given.

It was more difficult to believe that He was with Mortimer, who had driven Purdie to his wrong-doing. But had He not been with me when I had caused others to stumble? He did not have patience with me which He denied to other men. Mortimer and I stood together. I could see in him things which ought to be spoken against; but not spoken against by me as if it were my judgment. I had been angry with him in the past; but it had been in the words of my own anger. I needed now to speak to him in the words of judgment and mercy spoken to both of us alike.

I needed Mortimer, as he needed me. That had been unbelievable. Yet it was that and nothing less that I now had to believe. Mortimer had the Spirit, however much he might shut his ears and harden himself—he shut his ears and hardened himself only because of the presence of the Spirit. Some of his anger was anger against what the Spirit of God was asking of him; and some of it anger against himself because he knew that he had refused what God had spoken in his heart. And something of what God was speaking to him might at any moment break out to be God's word to me.

We were under the same forgiveness—I had believed that. We had to learn together, be quickened together—that I had not believed. We had both sinned; Christ had died for our forgiveness—I knew that. But—more difficult to me—the Spirit was given to us both. We had to learn from one another—he with the sins and needs I did not know, I with the sins and needs he did not know—what the Spirit was saying to us. I could not submit myself to God without submitting myself to him.

This was the Church—where Mortimer and I met, where God spoke to us both together.

17

I WAS seeing some little way into the mystery that we are bound together, in the end, not by what we are as men but by what God is doing for us. The kinship of the Church becomes stronger than any other.

When I went to the succour of a brother I was never coming there first; I was always taking the little I had where God was giving His all. When I prayed it was always for one in whom God was already at work. When I went to speak Christ's word I went as an interpreter of what He was already saying within; I did not break new ground. And if I wondered why then I should be needed at all I could remember that I myself had needed the word of one young in the Faith to make me hear what had been spoken in my heart for years.

It is part of the mystery of the Kingdom that we need our brother for our own saving. That is why there is the Church, and why it must begin as a Church where man submits himself to man. I had needed John Forsyth to help me to understand the Cross of Christ. I had needed Purdie to help me to understand a Father's care. I had needed Mortimer to help me to believe in the Spirit of God indwelling in every one of us. I needed those to whom I went because of their need. Without them I could not be sanctified; without them I could not be Christ's minister. I needed them, the unworthy as well as the worthy for God was with them all. He was saving us together.

How else was I able, when I had prayed, in the heat of anger against a man, for grace which I did not have in my heart, suddenly to lay my hand upon his arm, when he was delivered into unexpected meeting with me, and to say in my heart " Brother " ?

How else did it happen that, when I prayed for a man from whom I was estranged, a difference came about in his attitude to me and in mine to him without the saying of a word ? Was it coincidence, or some form of thought transference—or the work of the Spirit ? I had no doubt. Nothing authenticated more clearly for me that what was done in Galilee and Judea was being done now in Crainie. He was there. I saw His work as clearly as if He had stood before me.

I knew it was for this, above all, that I had been sent to be minister to this people. I was to stand in the midst of their need—and how else but as one in greatest need of all ? How else could I receive the word for their need except as myself a needy man . . . "as poor, yet making many rich; as having nothing, yet possessing all things " ?

The servant is not greater than his lord. The Christ had stood in the waters of Jordan, making Himself one with the company of sinful men; and He had said " Ye shall indeed be baptised with the baptism that I am baptised with."

That should be one of the compelling signs of His Church— that we are standing with Him where He stands in baptism; ourselves sinful men saved by the sinless one, but baptised with Him into the saving of others; standing with men in their sinfulness, yet facing God for them like Him.

One night, on my way to a visit from which everything in me recoiled, I knew suddenly that this new impulse was upon me. I was going to be with a man who had sinned greatly, to put my sinfulness beside his, and, by the strange miracle, at the

same time to be there also with Christ in His saving power;
to stand in common need, and be the means of its answering.
And I was going for love of Him.

It was the motive assumed in every minister; it was implied
in the vows of ordination which I had taken; but it was only
now being born in me; or perhaps it was being re-born.

There were some in Crainie, not called as ministers, in
whom I had seen this love shining. Where another might try
to act forgivingly because it was the Christian thing to do,
Sim would go the second mile in forgiveness because Christ
was standing there already. He would take a servant girl into
his house, not because she had a good record but because she
needed a new start, and because he believed she had been sent
there for him to help; Christ was standing by her, else she
would never have been there. He would endure some wrongs
said of him with quietness of spirit because he remembered
how much more Christ was suffering in it; he would stand
with Him in the same baptism.

I knew that Sim would never set out on a new venture
without a word that would help to make sure that it was " as
He wished"; and no perplexity would come upon him without
the simple word " Lord, I don't know what to do." It seemed
natural to him to stand with his Lord. But sometimes he
would say to me " I'm not a good man, minister. I'm rough,
rough . . ." The tenderness may have sprung from a rougher
ground than anyone knew.

Not so far away from us in Crainie there was a minister like
Sim. He was a familiar figure in the poor back streets of his
parish in an industrial town, looking for the men and women
to whom Christ would lead him because they were broken and
in despair.

He was led to many places where no other minister had

gone—to the cells in the local police station, to the corners where women looked for men, to the public-houses when they emptied their late drinkers on to the street; to places more respectable where they had never heard a man declare the love of God.

By going where he had no need to be, but where he was sure Christ was, he found what no one else had found. And as he went, with his shuffling steps, along the pavements and up the dingy stairs, men and women knew it was no ordinary love that was seeking them.

Was it this love that was being born in me? Sometimes it seemed enough just to stand before God, thankful for Him, thankful that love was there, thankful for what His love does and what it will not do; thankful even to put myself where I knew I might be made to suffer because a secret sin was being brought into the light of His countenance; and thankful that, whatever else there is in life, there is the certainty of this Kingdom of love at the heart of all, and that nothing can take it away, nothing can overcome it.

A ministry was being given back to me now which was not my own; a love and a joy, and a thankfulness for the miracle that he who has so little to give can be serving the Lord of heaven and earth.

There was laughter in it, too, as when I prayed that I might be used in the service of Christ's compassion, and a steady succession of needy folk came to my door at inconvenient hours, just as I had planned to be giving myself to the Lord's work; and when I prayed to be taught in Christ's patience, and a woman was sent to me time after time who wearied me in my well-doing and seemed to be only hindering me from important things.

I think I was beginning to understand why it had been

said to the disciples in the beginning " Be not ye called Rabbi."
All that they were was of the grace of God. If they had
become leaders of men it was because they were " chief of
sinners," one with the motley crowd in Jordan—and men are
not called " Rabbi " for that. If they had distinction amongst
their brethren it was because they had been like a brand
plucked from the fire—and men do not give honour for that.
We who come after them may be honoured for our learning
by those who wish to honour learning; we may be given titles
by those who wish to make recognition of some service to the
community. But if our sole merit lies in what God has done
for us, if we are indeed nothing but for Him, and are baptised
with Christ into all that we are, how can we take honour upon
us as if it were our achievement?

In these days the assurance which a little learning and
experience bring was being broken down. It had been one of
the means by which I concealed from myself that, day by day
and hour by hour, I was dependent upon God alone for all
my light. I was having to learn the mystery of being emptied
of striving yet empowered to work the works of God, of being
nothing before Him yet filled with the fulness of His grace. I
had come where I had nothing to give to those with whom I
stood but my empty hands, held out as if they had a power to
help that was not in them. Even with my knowledge of the
Word of God—I could come here at first only with the
poverty which its riches had laid bare ... " as having nothing."
This was one of the signs that we were standing with the
Christ who " emptied Himself and made Himself of no
reputation."

It had been like that from the beginning. Joy had been in
the hearts of men and women upon whom the Spirit had come;
but it was a joy born of the Cross and the cry on the Cross,

a joy which came to them when they knew that what they wanted to be they could never be, what they wanted to do they could never do—but He could do it; He could give it; He had won it. And the new life had come first to a few people in a corner of a land as small as ours, living under the same conditions as their neighbours, doing the same work, a little company baptised with Christ's baptism, " a little flock " to whom the Father was pleased to give the Kingdom. What had happened then was difficult for the mind to grasp because it was something which happened when the mind had reached the end of its resources and had nothing more to say. It had to be described in words mysterious to any who had not themselves entered in.

When it happened today to a few people in a small corner of our own land it was still as difficult for the mind to grasp, for it broke the mind's wisdom and made it begin again as a child; and it sent men to stand with those who seemed to have nothing in common with them.

It was difficult for John Forsyth. His temperament had been well-known in Crainie. He knew that its people had the measure of him and of his moods which had driven him to wildness of speech. He had to stand amongst them with a new life in him, knowing that there would be surprise when the expected retort did not come, seeing in their faces the expectation of it, hearing the embarrassed silence which awaited it. Somehow he had to learn to act in that moment without self-consciousness when they were self-conscious, and without letting himself slip back into feeling that they were against him because they looked strangely at him. Into the gap in conversation where he would have thrust his anger he had to begin thrusting new kinds of words. He had to face the look of surprise in his neighbours and bear the hurt of it, till they had become accustomed to a John Forsyth they had never seen before.

It was difficult for Jacob Telfer, finding his way into a new life at home, having to stand with friends at the market and be accosted as if he were still the same man, ready to do as he had been accustomed to do for as long as they could remember.

It was difficult for Purdie, standing with people who, he knew, had been angered at him, when the look in their eyes kept telling him that he might still prove himself to be no better than he had been, while he was trying to believe that old things were passed away. His baptism was to remain where he had been despised.

It was difficult for Kenneth Sanderson, with all the business methods and procedures created out of long experience. He could begin a new life, but he had to begin it standing in his office, where every relationship was set in the old ways.

They all, and others like them, had indeed to be baptised with the baptism that Christ was baptised with.

And it is no easier for the minister. He stands with the people of Crainie as their friend; yet even the friendliness can be a snare, as it had been in my first days in the parish. He may not be able to get past it—or he may not try to get past it—with the words which God has given him to speak. He tries to draw the young people to the Church by appealing to them to help in its work—and he may give them, as I had given Kenneth, only a sense of duty when they need to be brought to Christ. He enlists the business men in the Church's affairs and gives them the opportunity of service—only to find that in their hands the need for caution and carefulness can be magnified till it becomes the congregation's strongest temptation.

We are afraid, often, to be Christ's poor men. We hesitate between the wisdom of the world and His wisdom, daunted by the weight of the evidence. But we are not to be anxious. We are to learn to act even while we are daunted. We are to forgive seventy times seven even while our mind is still in debate whether this will be encouraging a man to think he can do as he likes with us, or is the only way to redeem him from evil. We are to go the second mile with the man who compels us to go one mile with him, while one part of our mind is telling us that this may be a sure way to incite him to make greater demands upon us.

We are to be prepared to stand with the sceptic and feel the pressure of his doubt—how prayer can affect anything in a world like this, with its interlocking events, and every man in a chain of necessity—and forthwith go to our praying because the world does look like this. We are to be prepared to have our own doubts how a few men and women can sway the future when it seems so clearly to be in the hands of the masses—and go straight to where two or three are gathered together in Christ's name, because the doubt is on us.

We are to learn the simplicity which takes Christ at His word. If Christ has promised that where two or three are gathered together in His name there He will be in the midst— then there will He be. If Christ has said that He will be in the Sacrament under the veil of the bread and the wine, as certainly there as they, we are to believe in the presence as surely and as simply as we feel the touch of bread and wine on our lips. If we are given a sudden impulse, no more than a flash in the mind, that there is someone to whom we are meant to go, somewhere that we are being sent, then there we will go, even if it is against our inclination—like Ananias, led along the street called Straight to say " Brother Saul," and Peter sent to Cornelius at Cæsarea, with whom it was unlawful for him to keep company.

It is this fixing of the eye on the immediate thing bidden, this refusal to turn back, this joyful abandonment to the divine love, which makes us instruments in God's hands.

This is our calling—to go out with decisive step even while we are in hesitancy, to go to the act of thanksgiving before we know we are healed, to distribute Christ's bread to the hungry before we know it will be sufficient. It is not for us to learn certainty but to learn to trust ourselves to God, and to do what we know He is expecting of us while we are still uncertain; to commit ourselves to Him hour by hour through our very weaknesses, through the very circumstances which would otherwise be for our hurt, the mischances, the limitations— so that all things begin to work together for good. There can be no circumstance so frustrating that it cannot be made the means of committing us more closely to Him.

18

ONE THING I knew. This handful of men and women in Crainie, with their minister, had been turned " from the power of Satan to God."

We had come where there was nothing more we could do about ourselves. We were lost. The farther we saw into ourselves the more we knew of the evil that was there, deeper than we could understand—always behind our good impulses the shadow of being aware of ourselves as good; and the loss of our purity. None of us would now have rejected Paul's words, " the body of this death," as a description of our state.

John Forsyth, Mary Plenderleith, Purdie, Mortimer, Jacob Telfer and his wife, Kenneth Sanderson and his father, the shepherd at Glenconnar, David Sim at the Brae, the family where young Malcolm was learning to face what was in us all, knowing that he was not standing alone; these and others too, and the minister in his manse—we had been where we could catch sight of what was fighting against God for the souls of men; and in the flash of seeing ourselves under that power we had known that our eyes had been opened, and who it was that had opened them. The despair and the deliverance were almost one; the hopelessness and the faith.

It had happened in the inmost solitariness of our being; our prayer was only a muffled cry from the heart—and yet none of us had been alone at these moments. It was when I had found myself brother to John Forsyth in a common sinfulness that the cry had broken from me. It was when I had sat with Jacob and Mary Telfer, realising myself suddenly no better than they, that my cry for them and my cry for myself had become one, and heaven was opened for common blessing.

When John Purdie was brought into the farmhouse at the Brae and made to sit down as a friend he could have cried out for sorrow at what he had been making of himself, because he knew in the instant that there was no barrier between himself and David Sim.

We had been baptised into Christ's baptism. We knew it because it was when we stood with other men, not condemning them but setting ourselves in our sinfulness beside their sinfulness and looking in common need to Christ's saving, that the baptism of the Spirit was given.

It was a baptism with fire because it began to burn up in us the self we had been, and to kindle in our hearts the love of God for all men, even those who were our enemies. We had been given, with our forgiveness, "an inheritance with them that are sanctified." We had become chosen vessels for the saving of others. There was the man beside us, the neighbour whom we had often met but never known, because we could be to him no more than our relationship to Christ enabled us to be; and we had been keeping back part of the price of fellowship. There were those out beyond to whom we would be sent to speak what we were bidden; and, beyond them, the world of unknown men and women where Christ was adding to the Church daily " those that were being saved."

I knew that it had been given to me, too, to minister as these others were not called to minister. There had been fulfilment of the grace promised in the laying on of hands at my ordination; not a greater work for me to do, perhaps a work more humble, but a special work—as though I were beseeching men " in Christ's stead," lifting up His bread and His cup for Him. For this that had happened was more than the creation of new men and women; it was the creation of the Church. We who had nothing in common had become a little community of the Spirit of God.

The great Church, concerned with the ordinances of religion and their establishment in the nation, has often been uncertain about this life of the Spirit within it, coming and going like the wind, blowing as it listeth, and no man knowing whence it cometh and whither it goeth.

The great Church has ensured the preaching of the Gospel and the administration of the Sacraments in every parish. however poor or remote, as no sporadic companies of Christians could have done. But always the tendency has been there to encourage its congregations to be successful branches of a central organisation; and the result has been to reproduce the kind of congregation which has the strongest temptations to conform with the world, as the great Church is tempted to do, instead of being the new creation, the new community of Christ, an advance post of the Kingdom.

I had learned in Crainie beyond all doubting that the Church is always being re-born in these companies of the few. But I was only beginning to understand the travail of its re-birth. For we who are called to take no reckoning of success are ourselves placed where success is expected of us; we who are to count the world well lost for Christ's sake are ourselves looked to for the maintaining of the Church's position in the world.

If we have the great Church set at the heart of the nation's life we must be concerned for its security. If we have a parish system its ministers must have a care for the increase of their congregations—and at once they are under temptation to think of what increases as necessarily good and what divides as evil (though Christ has said " Suppose ye that I am come to give peace? Nay, rather, division ") and to achieve the compromises by which human societies are welded together when the Gospel tells us that our dissatisfaction with these compromises is to be a main motive in making us seek the Kingdom. So it comes about that the cross is laid on us, often, not by the world outside but by those who dip with us in the same Lord's dish.

There is no tension, such as Christ predicted, between the " world " (when it is the law-abiding, moral world) and the Church as an institution working for righteousness, ordered according to upright business standards, directed by democratic methods, and maintained for the ultimate good of the nation. It is only in those who know they are called to something beyond goodness that tension appears.

How are they, this little Church within the great Church, to take no account of their safety and security and yet be anxious for the Church's safety and security? How are they to safeguard the institution and its property at every turn, protect it against all eventualities, and yet be the kind of people who will risk their local church property by bringing in the man who has an easy conscience about appropriating other people's goods? Crainie had come to the edge of that dilemma.

There is no problem at all, no tension, no division, unless we are the kind of people who are befriending the undesirable and bringing him in. There is no problem for the great Church. It is only in the two or three, gathered together in Christ's name to learn to love as He loves, that the dilemma appears. Or perhaps there is this problem for the great Church:

whether it is going to encourage the birth of the little Church within it or not, whether it is going to make provision for these companies of people who will bring the division into its midst.

The Church which has come down to us in our own land is a democratic Church. In all its courts rule is by the majority. Yet here is another principle thrust into the heart of its democracy: ·that few there may be who are finding the strait gate and the narrow way; that the Church is saved by its " remnant," as Israel was.

This is a hard thing for a Church in which the many decide what the Church shall be, where it shall go, what it shall renounce, and for what it shall be willing even to give up its life. This is the sword thrust into a Church which seeks to bring men in from the highways so that God's house may be filled, and then gives them the voice to over-rule what He is making known.

Why should there be this " remnant," this little Church, at all, bringing such division into the peace of the fellowship? The New Testament might seem at first to make us ask instead, why there should be the great Church at all, rooted and grown in the life of the world.

There is no doubt what we see in the beginnings: companies of believing people, nurtured in the homes of the " quiet in the land," the inheritors of the faith of the remnant in Israel, waiting on the Lord's word, learning a difficult obedience in welcoming to their fellowship men who had persecuted the Church of God, men who were despised in their communities, men of other races who were not accepted in the religious community. They are held together in their little companies, tempted all the time to be content with being good men, yet always urged on to something beyond what men called good, into a new undiscovered country of the spirit, wrestling with the problem of the obedience they owe to the State and the community, and the higher obedience they owe to Christ. The tension is there all the time, as Christ had warned them it would be. But this was how they knew they were truly His Church; this was the authentic mark of it. They were " born out of due time," because they believed the Kingdom was there and not in an ideal future or in another world.

" Not many wise, not many mighty, not many noble "— that was how the Church looked. Not much peace, if you thought of peace as an absence of strife—that was how it felt to be the Church. But they were not anxious.

They were not easily shocked. They were accustomed to being where life looked ugly and sordid. They were the kind of people in whom evil came up to the surface to be cleansed. All the disinclination to love their enemies, and to forgive seventy times seven the men who had wronged them, had to come out in words, in differences, in rebuke, in confession, in reconciliation. It did not give the Church the appearance of an easy fellowship, achieving its purpose with a clear eye for where it was going. And the more closely they followed their Master the hotter temptation became.

The twelve themselves had been no pattern of easy comrade-ship. They had disputed; they had wanted the wrong things; they had failed often. But they had learned, been disciples.

These had always been the marks of the Church whenever it continued to be in small companies in which men came within that kind of range of one another. They did not need to go out into the world to seek encounter with evil; they met it within the fellowship, where it was being brought under Christ's control. The conquest of the world outside was only

an extension of the victory which He was winning within
His Church.

They did not want, by natural impulse, to have all sorts and
conditions of people within; they did not have a natural
instinct to treat slaves on equal terms—this was what they were
taught, against the grain of their human nature; and they
learned it because they were together where men's hearts
were open to one another and to Christ.

It had been there from the beginning, this little Church.
As the great Church became necessary to establish the Faith in
the kingdoms of the world, to set it in the heart of nations as
well as individuals, the test of its fidelity was still found here—
did it prepare the way of the Lord where He was with the
two or three gathered together, even at the cost of creating a
" remnant " which would embarrass its greatness and contra-
dict many of the assumptions of its wisdom? For the little
Church is a ferment. It is the light which shows up everything
in the house.

This must always be the test of the great Church, its justi-
fication or its condemnation; and there have been many
times when it has failed by these standards.

As I considered my own Church and the temptations and
failures of my ministry in Crainie, it seemed to me that we had
been in such a time in our own land. But we were being given
back the Church we had lost—and perhaps being led towards a
Church we had never known. We were being raised up again;
saved, as of old, by the few. The future of the Church was with
them, though the rule of the majority might make their way
hard. But it is the little flock, learning obedience in the little
things and becoming one with all who love the Lord, that is
told not to fear. It is to them that the Father gives the first
promise of the Kingdom.

19

As I came near Crainie once, after some weeks' absence, and had my first sight of its hills and the distant outline of its woods and roads, a thankfulness broke upon me such as the Old Testament patriarchs must have known when they said of a place " Here the Lord was with me," and gave it a new name of their own as a memorial.

In that glen, amongst those hills, below that fir wood, I had come to know all that I now lived by. Beside that stream God had spoken to me. On that road He had made Himself known. Beneath that roof He had saved me. The whole scene was woven into the pattern of what He had done. " Here I prayed —and here I was answered."

When I could just make out the white walls of the manse amongst its lime trees I remembered how it could be also within a man's home. It could seem that God had searched out, not the one who would bring easy congeniality to him but the one through whom purity of heart might be given to him who had known no such purity, and honesty to him who so often failed to be truthful in the hidden parts; and the sudden realisation would come that this could be no chance. Here was the very thing in the woman who loved him which he had failed to be, the kind of love which he had made impossible for himself, the love of which he had proved himself unworthy.

The providence which we find it hard to discern in the sweep of great events is often revealed in the shaping of two lives. The little decisions, which lead to the great, are also in His hand: the moment of choosing what seems unimportant, the planning of a journey, the invitation of a friend. He knows the way we take, or He could not, by the slenderest of human chances, bring two of us together for our saving. He had girded me even when I had not known Him. He had been with me in my unbelief.

The whole mystery of the divine love could be reflected like this in one home, as for Hosea the deepest meaning of forgiveness had come out of his broken home. We could know the very things of which a man had proved himself unworthy given back to him one by one, opposite for opposite, his forfeited self restored to him piece by piece, the past not merely blotted out but redeemed.

This is the sign, too, of what He does for us within His Church.

I had begun my ministry in Crainie in a great uncertainty, unworthy of my calling; and He had accepted me with the uncertainty upon me, and given it back to me as a grace to enter into the uncertainties of others and learn Christ's certainty along with them.

This is His love for us: that His grace is fashioned for each to meet his special need; that we receive where we have been least worthy to receive; that where we have been weak there we are made strong with a strength which is not for ourselves alone. This is the miracle of the Church.

It is no shadowy life beyond for which we are being prepared. It is a life with all the marks on it of the life we now know, the life of our homes, the life of our work. The love of God which is concerned with these things in us here is saving us for a life where these things are not lost.

" There's anither Crainie," old Margaret Plenderleith used to say to me. There is what Crainie has drawn out of the heart of God, the imprint of the life of every man, woman and child in Crainie upon His heart, His compassion for each moment of their need each day—so that the life of every one of us might be seen reflected in this urgency that bends over us in warning, and this patience that encourages us till every spark of good has become a flame.

If it were all to be added together, as our minds might try to add it, moment by moment, life by life, there would be " anither Crainie " more real than the Crainie men can see, a Crainie in the heavens, part already of the eternal life of God. It was like the clouds that lay for a moment on the rough hill-tops of Crainie and then passed away to become part of the distant horizon, with the shapes of Cardon and the Fell still upon them, shining in the western sky, homely and familiar, but translated into glory.

" Anither Crainie " is already there. It is no ethereal vision. It is as familiar as the life of Crainie every day, for it is made up of His dwelling with us, His thoughts alongside our thoughts, His mind stooping to the understanding of our minds, His will bent to the saving of us as each danger threatens us. Yet it is the Crainie of God, shining with eternal glory. It is a Crainie more real than the Crainie men know, for the love of God is more real than the evil it has overcome; and the life that a man now lives, " hid with Christ in God," is already more real than the life of outward appearance. It is our life, yet it is His life, our life given back to us transmuted by His forgiveness and His grace, our waywardness worked into the pattern of His purpose—an inheritance in the heavens that passeth not away.

But this love of God, which has the marks on it of all that

we have been, as the hands of the risen Christ had upon them the marks of the nails, is a consuming fire. It must, by its very passion, destroy all evil at the last, and whatever has part in evil. It is a love which is building a new Crainie; but it must destroy by its fire the Crainie men have made, and whatever in Crainie will have no part in the Kingdom.

If we could see through to the "ither Crainie," beyond the veil of this life, there would be urgency on us all like the urgency which brought Rob Brunton to the Kirk on Sacrament Day, broken and bedridden and unable to work out a better life for himself, carried on an old stretcher by his friends and laid in the passage-way—clutching at the mercy of God and taking into his hands the bread and the cup of all that he did not deserve to receive, all he could never do for himself and all he could never atone for in what he had done to others, and finding the mercy given.

DATE DUE
